‚5-04

TO FRANCES —

Best Wishes

Don

Gift of

Frances McWilliam

Rough Sketches

SHORT STORIES OF A TRAVELING ARTIST

DON ANDREWS

Rough Sketches
Short Stories of a Traveling Artist
By Don Andrews

Published by:
Andrews Publishing
Post Office Box 677
Exeter, NH 03833

Printed in the United States of America

Library of Congress Control Number: 2002096501

ISBN 0-9655559-1-7

Cover photo and design by Martha Andrews
Back cover photo by Mollie Bullock

In Memory Of

Helen Andrews

V.Y. "Tex" Fowler

Robert E. Wood

I can do all things through Christ
Who strengthens me.

Philippians 4:13

Be good
And you will be lonesome
Be lonesome
And you will be free
Live a lot
And you'll live to regret it
That's what living means to me
That's what living means to me

Mark Twain
Jimmy Buffett

These stories would reside only in my mind if not for the encouragement, direction and editing skills of my dear friends;

Judith Richards and C.Terry Cline

Jess, Dan, Mollie, and Jake,
you are your mother's greatest
gift to me.

*This book and everything else in my life
is dedicated to Martha.
I feel sorry for anybody who's
not me.*

Contents

Introduction

The week I was scheduled to teach a workshop in Dallas, I had left Boston's Logan Airport on a late afternoon flight, connecting through Atlanta. By the time I arrived in Dallas, picked up my luggage, and was delivered to my hotel, it was late and I was beat.

At the front desk of my hotel, I was greeted by an attractive black woman in her mid 40's, who was cordial and attentive, but obviously new at her job. She had a terrible time on the computer finding my reservations, and in general, struggled through every step of the usual check-in procedure, all the while under the constant, and none too compassionate eye of the night manager. Surrounded by luggage, I leaned on the front desk and tried not to act impatient. Did I want smoking or non, first floor or up, king size or double? I didn't say so, but at that moment I'd take any room with a bed.

She finally handed me my card key with an apology for the delay, explaining the obvious, that she was new on the job.

"That's okay," I said, "in a week you'll be able to do all of this blindfolded." We exchanged haggard smiles and I departed.

Finally in my room, I wanted to relax and take off my shoes, but there was one more demon to deal with before I undressed for bed. I quit smoking December 1st, 1996. I also stopped smoking a couple of times in January '97, and quit for good several times more in February. It was now March. I pulled out of my breast pocket a slightly bent Camel I had bummed earlier that day from a stranger in Atlanta, telling myself that this was going to be my last cigarette.

I had ordered a non-smoking room as proof of my new status, so I decided to walk up and down the hall while I smoked. The way I explained this to myself is that smoking is bad for you, walking is good for you, so combining the two equals things out.

As I paced the empty corridors, I began to wonder why life was so tough on me. Everyone I knew had a regular job and was home in bed right now, while I was stuck all alone in some strange hotel on Saturday night.

As I approached a doorway, I recognized the lady from the hotel front desk, handing a bucket of ice to the occupant of a room adjacent to mine. As I passed, I heard her say, "Thank you," and she turned right beside me as I walked by. Finding ourselves in the awkward position of suddenly walking side by side, we exchanged greetings, took a few steps in silence, and then she said, "Do you think it's all right to accept a tip for delivering ice to a room?"

"Sure," I said, trying not to blow fumes in her face. "People expect to tip for room service."

"Well, I guess you're right," she sighed, half speaking to the dollar she held out in her hand, "at least something's gone right today."

"Had a rough one?"

"Oh, I don't want to spout my troubles to you, it's just that someone stole my purse today, and I pretty much lost everything. Grocery money, driver's license, credit cards and to top if off, I'd made out my monthly bills to mail and they're gone too!"

"Have you called the police?"

"Police, credit card office, landlord, you name it, I've been on the phone most of the afternoon, but I can't reach the bank or utilities until Monday."

"All that and a new job too."

"Well, this is my night job, moonlighting," she said. "I'm a single parent and I can sure use the money, but I worry so about leaving the kids alone nights, with all the trouble out there these days."

We had reached the elevator and she stopped to push the button.

"I'm sorry to be going on," she said. I could see the weight she carried, reflected in her dark eyes.

I paused beside her, holding my cigarette behind my back, as if she wouldn't notice the smoke, no doubt curling up around my ears. I wanted to give her some brief word of comfort, some reassurance, but the usual clichés seemed hollow, so we stood there in silence until a bell rang and the door clanked open. "Bless your heart," I whispered.

She nodded her head in thanks. "I'll make it," she said. A moment later, the elevator doors closed and she was gone.

Up and down the hallways in the late night silence I pondered as I paced. Each time I came to my room number, I passed it by again. What could this brave woman teach me about the challenges of life? How long had she stood on tired feet today? There'd be no room service where she slept.

I've been so lucky in life, doing what I do, traveling the country teaching painting workshops. My life in art has been like a dream world of travel and painting. I've seen the sunsets in Sedona and walked the redwood forest of Northern California. I once had lunch in the Space Needle in Seattle, and I've put my hand on the Liberty Bell. From the Grand Canyon to the Great Lakes, from Monterey to Myrtle Beach, and the best part of it all has been the people; so many wonderful, and a few not so wonderful, unique characters, no two quite the same.

My memories of my travels are filled with people. I've spent years secretly studying how they act and react. I have no degree in Psychology; I don't have a clue as to what makes them tick, I just like to watch the ticking. Someone once told me that I should write it all down...so I did.

Judge Andrews

"On behalf of our state watercolor society," Janet said over the phone, "I'd like to invite you to serve as judge for our annual exhibition." I've always enjoyed judging painting competitions, so I readily accepted. "Oh, there's one more thing," she added, "would you be willing to do a live interview at the exhibition reception, for a local TV station?"

"Why not?" I said.

When the dates rolled around on my calendar, I arranged for my flight to arrive early enough to be picked up at the airport by Janet and driven directly to the museum where my jury duty was to be done. Clipboard in hand, I meandered through aisles of paintings lined up side by side along the museum floor. The show contained a wide variety of formidable pieces from which to choose, so once the inevitable sifting process was completed, I felt good about my award selections.

The following evening Janet picked me up and drove me to the museum for the exhibition's opening reception. The accepted paintings now hung on the museum walls, with colored ribbons gracing the award winners. A stick-on nametag marked "Judge Andrews" was stuck on my lapel. Janet asked me to stay close by in case anyone had questions, and reminded me that the television people would shortly be arriving for our promotional TV interview.

"Oh, yes, the interview," I scolded myself as I stood there, feeling the first pangs of anxiety. I'm always so sure of myself months before when I'm asked to do this sort of thing. Then the time arrives to perform and my tongue gets tied in a Gordian knot. I tried to reassure myself. Things had gone well so far; the people had been cordial, the show was pleasing. My palms might be a little sweaty, but I'd be all right!

Shortly the TV crew arrived. I was introduced all around and told by Ms. Jackson, the journalist doing the interview, that they would be ready for me in about thirty minutes. "Just relax," she instructed, "the secret to live TV is to be prepared. I'll ask you a few simple questions about your impressions of the show. Keep your answers short and you'll be fine, Mr. Uh..."she glanced down to my lapel, "Judge Andrews."

As the crew bustled about setting up lights, cameras and gear, I stood by trying to look contemplative as I nodded and smiled at the flow of viewers who were proceeding into the museum. This standing around, looking judicial as you smile and nod at total strangers, does require a particular flair and if I say so myself, I can smile and nod with the best of them!

Every two minutes I'd glance down to check my watch as my interview anxiety spiked up another notch. I ran down my list of what not to say, compiled from past disasters. "Don't try to be funny, don't go into too much detail, don't say anything…"

My thoughts were interrupted as I made eye contact with a sturdy looking older gentleman approaching me. His muscular neck supported a large head with hair cropped in a military flat top. Steel-gray eyes and a well-trimmed mustache gave him the look of a giant English terrier. I returned his gaze with a smile and a first rate nod. Stepping up to me, he glanced down at the label of judge posted on my jacket and all pretense of cordiality fell from his hardened face.

"You the judge?" he snapped.

"Yes sir, my name is Don Andrews. How do you do?"

"Why?"

I wasn't exactly sure what he was asking me, why was I Don Andrews? "Why?" I asked.

"Why in heaven's name would you select something like that?" he said, pointing over my shoulder to a half sheet abstract painting with an honorable mention ribbon.

Unclear as to where his questions were leading, I thought perhaps he wanted a better understanding of abstract art.

"Well sir," I began, "in order to appreciate abstract organization, you must..."

"What is it?" he huffed.

Clearing my throat I tried again. "You see, abstract..."

Instantly he cut me off.

"Pray tell," he bellowed, veins popping red, "what does that... that thing mean?"

Now things were clearing up. He wasn't looking for education. My thoughts on the virtues of abstract organization were of no interest whatsoever. About then I also realized that my earlier terrier description was somewhat off the mark. There before me was a bulldog with a bad tooth snarling in my face! No, he wasn't looking for enlightenment, what he wanted was a pound of my flesh!

"Hanging just over there," he pointed to an adjacent wall, "is a beautifully painted barn scene, with every rusty nail as realistic as can be! I'll have you know it took my wife two weeks to complete," he boomed, "and you passed it over for this...this...this thing!"

Mercifully at that moment, as I stood stammering, I was delivered from this mauling by an attractive, if somewhat embarrassed looking lady. She reached her arm across the back of the massive bulldog's jacket, gave me a wilted smile and him a gentle nudge.

"Come along, Raymond," she whispered from the corner of her mouth. Raymond's steely glare was still locked onto me when she patted his shoulder and nudged him once again. Snorting and fuming, he gave me a disgusted shake of his massive head, and in unison, they turned and walked away!

"Phew..." Once again, I stood alone. Momentarily undisturbed, I was now free to place my undivided attention on the piercing ache pounding in my forehead! "Well, Don," I told myself, "you certainly handled that nicely!" I took a couple of deep breaths. "Now calm down, nod...smile...."

A technician from the TV station waved to catch my attention, and then pointed to his watch. "Fifteen minutes," he said.

I felt my face pale and my mouth go dry. "Why do I get myself into these situations?" Suddenly, I was in need. What I needed was water, what I needed was air, what I really needed was a cigarette! Smiling and nodding, I made a break for the museum front door!

Once outside, cigarette ablaze, I had just enough time to contemplate the wisdom of giving live interviews on local TV stations. As I stood there trying to regain my composure, a stylish-looking younger couple walked by me as they exited the museum. The young man's sculpted beard and ponytail were accentuated with a gold earring. The young lady accompanying him wore an ankle length multi-colored sundress. Each step she took was punctuated with jingles from a multitude of turquoise and silver bracelets, necklaces and earrings.

My mind was elsewhere; my instincts took over. We made eye contact as they passed and, without thinking, I gave them a smile and, to make matters worse, I nodded as well!

Suddenly they paused. He looked at the somewhat tarnished label of *judge* on my jacket, and then they stepped over to me.

"So, you're the judge?"

"Yes," I answered. "I hope you enjoyed the show."

"Well, man, if you don't mind my saying so, some of your choices were a bit pedestrian!"

"I beg your pardon?"

"The realism is trite, man, it just doesn't belong in this century!"

Obviously enjoying my reaction, the young lady periscoped her head toward me with a "what do you say to that" expression on her face.

"Yeah!" she hissed, "the world doesn't need another pretty picture, man!"

Fumbling for the proper response, I was once again rescued from this assault by one of the TV assistants as he stuck his head through the museum door.

"Oh, there you are Mr....uhhh?" he paused glancing down at the smoldering nametag.

"Just call me Don, okay?"

"We're ready for your interview," he said, and pointed the way inside.

A cauldron of bile boiled in my stomach; pulsing veins rushed blood to my pounding temples. I excused myself from my smirking adversaries, and like a condemned man being led to the gallows, I silently followed the assistant through the museum front door.

Pointing his finger in the air, he coached me as we walked. "Remember this is live television so keep your answers short."

He didn't know it, but at the moment that was the only response I was prepared to guarantee.

Inside the main gallery, two chairs sat facing each other with the "Best of Show" painting hung on the wall between them. Huge lights mounted on tripods were aimed at the chairs. Loads of technical equipment, boxes and wires lay tangled on the floor. The correspondent, Ms. Johnson, was talking technical talk to an assistant. Upon seeing me, she gave a practiced smile, but there was a hint of concern in her eyes.

"Steve," she said, "get Mr...uhh..." she glanced down quickly at her notepad, "Andrews some water will you? Now just relax, live TV is a snap," she spoke in a calming tone. The assistant handed me a cone of water and we took our seats. "Steve, can you do something about his forehead?"

Ms. Johnson leaned forward in her chair and patted the air. "Don't worry," she whispered, "just follow my lead."

People milling around the museum stepped up to watch as everyone took their places. "Quiet please!" Steve shouted and then he pointed to Ms. Johnson. "Okay everybody, we're live in 3...2...1..."

On his cue, Ms. Johnson smiled into the camera. "We're broadcasting live this evening from the Civic

Museum, for the twelfth Annual Watercolor Exhibition. With us is nationally known artist, teacher, and judge…" Gracefully, she glanced down at the notes in her lap, "Mr. Don Andrews."

In unison, Ms. Johnson and the camera turned to focus on my ash-colored face.

"So, tell us Mr. Andrews, why should our viewing audience come out to see the twelfth Annual Watercolor Exhibition?"

Heart pounding, cheeks ticking, I tried to clear my throat. I gave her a wilted smile, followed by the faintest of nods.

"Everyone I've spoken to so far," I stammered, "can't say enough about the quality of the show!"

Country Music

I realize this admission isn't in keeping with the cultural persona that an artist is expected to project, but the truth is…I'm a big fan of country music. Now wait, if you haven't listened to your country music station lately; give it one more try. You'll be surprised at what's coming out of Nashville these days. Like Alan Jackson says, "We're not as backwards as we used to be."

I've got nothing against classical music, but when you find yourself in the Ramada Inn, out by the interstate late some night, Beethoven isn't going to take you where you need to go. On the other hand, Garth Brooks, *"I've got friends in low places where the whiskey drowns, and the beer chases my blues away…and I'll be okay…I'm not much on social graces…Think I'll slip on down to the Oasis, cause I've got friends…in low places."* Sorta gets you right there, doesn't it?

A few years back, I was teaching a workshop in a small coastal town in Northern California. Early in the week, I discovered a wonderful little Mexican restaurant within easy walking distance of my hotel. During workshops I usually go out to eat early. That's the only time most restaurants are quiet, the service good, and I can relax and catch my breath a bit. Sure enough, when I entered the restaurant shortly after 5 o'clock, the place was empty. The waiter quickly arrived and took my order for enchiladas. I sat back with salsa and chips and reflected on the day's events.

Soon, the waiter was back with my dinner. One look at my plate of enchiladas and I knew I'd picked the right spot. There's nothing I enjoy more when traveling out west than patronizing the vast variety of Mexican eateries and cantinas and California has some of the best. As I savored my treat, the screen-front western style door opened, and two young couples in tennis shorts and pinstriped shirts entered, engrossed in conversation. They took a table just across from mine. The tranquility I was enjoying instantly evaporated into idle chat involving stocks, bonds, deals on sports cars and doing business in Japan.

Since I don't own a sports car, and do very little business in Japan, I tried to ignore the high tech conversation as my eyes began wandering around the room. In the corner, by the front door, was a Wurlitzer Juke box. I decided that if I couldn't have quiet, then I would pick the noise. I got up from my dinner, walked over to the jukebox and began searching the singles for something to suit my mood. To my surprise, hidden in the mix of popular and rock singles was Travis Tritt's, "Here's A Quarter, Call Someone Who Cares," a sure enough, break you to your knees, country classic. I dropped a coin into the slot and pushed B 33, returned to my enchiladas, anticipating the reaction of my new found dining companions. To my delight, the volume of the jukebox was booming as Travis began belting out the syrupy lyrics in three quarter time. *"Call someone who'll listen and might give a damn, maybe one of your sordid affairs; you say you'd be happy if you could just come back home; here's a quarter call someone who...here's a quarter call someone who...here's a quarter call someone who..."*

OH NO! My heart sank... the needle on the Wurlitzer was skipping and catching, repeating the same refrain, over and over. *"Here's a quarter call someone who..."*

I caught the reaction of the eye-rolling yuppies all right, but it wasn't exactly what I had in mind. I sprang to my feet and tried to, nonchalantly, bolt over to the hiccuping Wurlitzer, giving it a good bump. Still the needle stuck and the blaring lyrics continued. I gave the box a second shove. The needle bounced, then came back to rest in the same groove, *"a quarter call someone who..."*

Now the yuppies were not only staring, but snickering as well. Glaring down at my tormentor, I squarely faced the box. With a firm grip on both shoulders of the blaring machine, I put my full weight behind my heave, lifting the front legs of the Wurlitzer off the floor. At once the lyrics were replaced by a high-pitched screech as the needle jumped the groove and grated across the record. The box fell silent at last; with a sigh of resignation, I turned and walked the long walk back to my table.

As best I could, I tried to avert my eyes from the four chuckling yuppies who had obviously enjoyed my calamity, and were now free to go back to enlightened conversation. I finished my meal as quickly as possible, made a mental note to explore a huge commodity investment in Central America, paid my bill and departed.

These little setbacks in life pass quickly, not so my taste for good Mexican food. About 5 o'clock two afternoons later, I found myself once again headed for the little Mexican cantina down the street. As before, I entered to find the establishment empty, the waiter cordial, and the aroma irresistible. I took my same table, ordered chili rellenos, sat back with salsa and chips, and my good friend and dining companion, solitude.

In no time, the waiter returned with my dinner. It was about that moment that my dining companion, solitude, tipped his hat, bid farewell, and removed himself from my table and the restaurant. As the swinging screen doors blew open, three hyperactive boys blasted in, wrestling, running and screaming, the likes of which the west has not seen since the Little Big Horn.

Presently, two ladies entered, enthralled in their own high volume conversation, oblivious to the hysteria going on around them. On one lady's hip perched a bucking toddler anxious to be free. The two women walked the length of the restaurant and settled at a table adjacent to mine. Instantly, the waiter produced a high chair for the toddler and took orders as the three hurricanes blew from one table to the next. Try as I might, it was impossible to ignore the tempest going on around me, though the two women seemed to have no trouble. They were so busy talking about what the little demons do, they were paying absolutely no attention to what the little demons were doing. Suddenly, one of the noisemakers flopped down in the chair next to me, grabbed a handful of chips, squealing with delight as he jumped up to make his escape.

"Now, Ricky, leave that man alone," came a shallow request from one of the women, who then rejoined her friend in conversation. Ricky was already circling for another pass. He was soon joined by his cohorts, and within minutes, I was relegated to refereeing a chip-stealing contest. Between attacks, I tried to gobble what was left of my chili relleno, before Ricky and his friends got more adventurous.

At that moment, a miracle happened; the waiter appeared before the two ladies bearing a platter overflowing with tacos and soft drinks. Ricky and his larcenous friends instantly lost all interest in me, sprang over to their mothers' table, where they were each presented with ample portions of MSG, sugar, and salt. Presto! A hush filled the restaurant as the feast began.

As I walked to the front door, I dropped a coin in the jukebox and made my selection. I stepped out into the cool California evening.

From inside the screen door came familiar lyrics that lifted my heart. "*...And you say you'd be happy if you could just come back home...Here's a quarter, call someone who...Here's a quarter call someone who...Here's a quarter, call someone who...*"

Higher Education

"One of the contributions our art group makes to the community," my workshop director, Ann, told me as we drove from the airport to my hotel, "is to allow a few promising students from our local university to attend our workshop free of charge."

"That's a great idea," I offered my approval. "They'll be full of idealistic enthusiasm about becoming an artist, just like we were at that age."

"Won't it be fun to see what the next generation of young artists are up to?" Ann said. I couldn't help but smile as I recalled my own romantic artistic notions, back in my art school days, some thirty odd years ago.

"No doubt," I said, "they'll be a refreshing addition to our class!"

The next morning among the rumble of people filing into the studio, I spotted two young men of about twenty years with untucked shirts and baggy pants. Immediately, they moved off by themselves and huddled in the corner. I approached them and introduced myself.

Rich was tall as a stork and thin as a reed. His eyes never left his shuffling feet, as he gave me a cold-fish handshake and mumbled what I thought was a greeting. John, on the other hand, was a compact muscular fellow who's piercing eyes glared from the shadows of the bill of his ball cap. He cocked his head and jutted his jaw. "Sup", he said. I have four teenagers at home, so I was instantly able to interpret his response. He had just said, "What's up," which can further be translated into the positive greeting, "How do you do." This is great I thought, as I walked away. We're off to a good start!

Monday morning is always the same in my figure-painting workshop.
Everybody's anxious and uptight. After an introductory talk, I start the class with a series of two-minute gesture poses to break the ice. I tell the group not to worry about getting their drawings just right, there'll be time for that later. The real goal is to loosen up.

As is my practice, I stroll around the class during this warm-up session. I make a comment or suggestion here and there, but really I'm just getting a feel for the students. As I approached the far side of the room, I spotted Rich and John behind easels, stationed as a partition between them and the rest of the class. I stepped around the easels and stood behind Rich as he worked, peering around his towering shoulder to his newsprint pad. There, on his paper, was a series of indistinguishable vertical slashes. This was a little looser than I had in mind, but I sensed that these two were uncomfortable in the company of strange adults, and I didn't want to start out sounding critical.

"That's provocative, Rich," I said. "Very energetic, but why not add a little form to the slashes to capture the gesture?"

Rich gazed down at his feet, shrugged his shoulders, and gave me a nod. Then I stepped over behind John. There, on his easel, sat an untouched page of newsprint paper. John stood staring at it with folded arms.

"John, don't worry," I prodded, "just jump in."

He spun around to face me with a hostile expression. "Hey man," he snapped, "I'm not into gesture drawing!"

"John," I said, "I've always found that if we take the time to loosen up with a series of gesture drawing, we can capture the model in the longer poses with a more personal line quality."

"Whatever," he said.

With that, I turned and walked away. John's remarks had stung me a little, but I told myself to be patient. They're just self-conscious, in unfamiliar territory. I'd give them space and they would come around.

After the warm-up session was over, I called the class together to do a painting demonstration on a concept I call "linkage," connecting the light and shadow patterns on the model to give the subject unity. Every minute or so, I'd pause during the demonstration to face the class and explain what I was trying to accomplish. Each time I turned to face the class, I couldn't help but notice the two young artists seated behind the last row of students. They whispered and nudged each other, gazed out the window, up at the ceiling or down to the floor. They made every effort to look anywhere in the room, except up front at me.

Once the demonstration was over, I sat the models in a single pose for one hour with model breaks every twenty minutes. After the first session was over and the second session began, I started my class rounds. Shortly, I made it over to the corner where the barricaded young painters stood. I stepped behind them and peered around Rich's shoulder to his paper. Once again, filled with a series of vertical slashes, only this time he used multi-colored paint!

"Rich," I asked, "What are you trying to do?"

Mute, Rich looked down to his shuffling feet and shrugged his shoulders. Next I stepped over to get a look at John's painting, which was totally different from Rich's. John's painting was a series of paint globs. Growing out of the top of one glob was a ghoulish head with arm-like appendages on either side.

"John, why not tie some of those parts together with some lines?"

"Hey man, I'm not into line, it's been done!"

"Okay, John, but if your drawing was more cohesive, you'd..."

He cut me off. "I'm not interested in drawing," he said. "I don't want my ability to get in the way of what I have to say!"

"But, John, isn't it true that you could convey your message to your audience more legibly, if you are able to articulate better?"

"Look dude, the more I explain, the less room for interpretation, comprende?"

"Fair enough, I'm all for personal expression. Picasso took incredible liberties with anatomy in order for his work to break out of the limitations of a single point of view, but beneath his interpretations was a powerful understanding of the human form. His drawings were masterful."

"Don't worry," John assured me, "I can draw, no problem!"

"I'll tell you what," I said, "this afternoon, after I finish my demonstration, we're going to have a single pose for the rest of the day. If you'll draw the figure realistically to show me you understand the human form as it is, then you can get as interpretational as you want for the rest of the week."

"Sounds like a waste of time, compadre, but if you say so, then it's a deal!"

I've never done an afternoon demonstration so fast. I couldn't wait to see how John would do. After I finished, I got the models to their podiums and told the class the pose would be for the rest of the afternoon. I sat back on my table and held myself in check to give John time to work. From across the room, I spied John out of the corner of my eye, poking his ball-capped head around the side of his easel to squint at the model. Then he disappeared for a moment before he popped out again. He was hard at work. I promised myself that I would be fair in my assessment of his work, but he better be good!

An hour and two model breaks passed before I made my way over to the corner barricade. With a great show of nonchalance, I first went to Rich's easel and made a perfunctory comment on his unique use of vertical slashes. After he'd mumbled an incoherent response, I stepped over behind John. There, on his easel, was a clumsy attempt at anatomical structure. The planes of the face were off; the head was too small for the torso, limbs hung without bones at odd angles. While I observed, John worked on drawing the right hand, then he'd erase, grumble, scribble, and erase some more.

As I suspected, John had spent more time playing artist than working at being one. I braced myself for an onslaught of excuses before I asked, "So, John, how's it going?"

To my dismay, he sounded pleased with his effort, defiant in his response. "See, man, I know what I'm doing, but I can't get this hand right."

"What seems to be the problem?"

"Ah, man, the model keeps moving!"

Very well, if these two were happy with their work, I'd let them go their own way. I wasn't going to ignore them though. My motives may have changed, but it would still be interesting to probe the minds of these two young recruits in the coming age of art!

The next day after the morning demo, I made my usual rounds to critique the class. When I came to Rich, I studied his painting silently for a moment before I spoke.

"Rich, nobody makes a vertical slash the way you do!" His shoulders bobbed up and down like pistons. "So tell me Rich, what period of art would you say has most influenced your work?"

Instantly, his shoulders rounded and he slowly shook his head. "I dunno," he mumbled.

"Aren't there any artists you admire?"

"Uhhh…. I guess Brackman's work is pretty cool."

"Good, Rich, but can you be a little more specific? Define cool for me?"

"Ahh….you know," he stammered, "his paintings are…are…far out!"

"I see, thank you for clearing that up. So you want your paintings to be far out?"

"Yeah, you got it!"

"Well, keep working, Rich, and I predict your paintings will be far out in no time!"

Next, I stepped over behind John and tried to assimilate the globs on his paper. "John, to what do you attribute your success as an artist?"

He cocked his ball-capped head. "I'm a senior, man. I've been at this for four years now."

"That's certainly impressive, John, so no doubt you've studied a wide variety of art periods and artists. Tell me whose work you admire?"

"Nobody, man," he shot back. "I don't want to be influenced. It blocks my originality!"

I countered his reasoning with a question. "Shouldn't we learn art the way we learn everything else? Study those who came before us, learn the basics, gain a visual vocabulary, so our work can speak with authority?"

John's shaded eyes narrowed as he slowly shook his head. "Naw, man, all that drawing, color and design stuff you old guys teach is counterproductive." Pausing to tug on the bill of his cap, he continued. "See man, art isn't about painting anymore, that's ancient history. Today, art is about making a statement." He pointed to his easel. "Take my painting for example, what's your gut reaction?"

"To tell you the truth, John," I offered a monumental understatement, "it's not very good."

John nodded his head in agreement, "You hate it, right?"

"That's putting it mildly, John, but, yes, I hate it."

"See, man," he pointed his finger at me like a pistol, "I'm doing a series of work on basic human emotions. Hate is one of the unique homosapien feelings I want my audience to tune in to when they view my art!"

"I'm sorry, John, but I'm not quite sure I follow."

"Don't you get it, man?" he said, with his hands in a palms-out gesture. "You're supposed to hate it!"

I had to admit, he had me boxed in. "If I'm supposed to hate it, John, then your painting is exceedingly successful!"

John accepted my compliment with a knowing shrug. "See man, you want your paintings to look good. I want my paintings to shake the world up. Look at how Andrew Serrano's "Piss Christ" grabbed the public's attention. People were outraged. That was a real turning point in Art History!"

"John, if you think the "Piss Christ" is a legitimate work of art," I said, " get me a cup of coffee, give me twenty minutes and I'll give you a demonstration!"

After the next morning's lesson, the class settled down to work. From my table across the room, I noticed Rich towering above the crowd. He appeared to mechanically put down a few brush strokes on his painting, then he'd step back and stiffen as if he were having a seizure. His arms fell limp by his sides as he stood at attention, eyes closed, face tilted toward the ceiling! A few moments passed, then his eyes popped open. He'd mix a swirl of paint in his palette and deliver it to his painting. Then, he'd step back, close his eyes and once again be seized by rigor mortis! Wide-eyed, I watched as Rich repeated this ritual over and over.

The anticipation of an explanation of this exercise so enthralled me that I practically jumped two easels and knocked over a paint tray to get by his side! "Rich," I stammered, trying to contain myself, "what are you up to?"

"Oh, hey dude," Rich muttered as if he were awakening from a trance. "I'm practicing the Zen method of painting."

"I see," I said as dispassionately as possible. My mind bristled with anticipation of the oncoming explanation. This had to be good. "Uhh…Rich, could you explain the Zen method of painting to me?"

"Sure man, my girlfriend, Carla, turned me on to it. The idea is, if you want to paint something, first you have to become it, comprende?"

"I'm not sure," I said. " In other words, you're saying that in order to paint a cloud, the artist must first become a cloud, in the mind's eye, is that it?"

"Right, man, you've got it."

I looked over to Rich's painting just under way; he was working on the face. "So, you're saying in order to paint the model's nose, you have to become the model's nose, is that right?"

"Contact, man, that's the deal."

"So how do you like it?"

Rich looked down and started shuffling his feet. "It's really, uh…really…"

"Far out?" I asked.

"Yeah, dude," he nodded. "It's far out!"

Now that I had gained some insight into John and Rich's painting perceptions, I began to look forward to my trips each day to the easel barricade. It was fun to try my hand at deciphering their paintings and hear their explanations and titles. I'd stand behind John, looking over his shoulder till he reached a stopping point and stepped aside. Silently, we'd stand as I pondered analysis. "Let me see, red streaks, and orange globs on a blue-black background. I've got it," I announced, "pride!"

"Naw, man."

"Okay, jealousy, right?"

"Nope."

"This doesn't have anything to do with mating habits does it?"

"No way."

"Good," I said. "You had me worried there for a minute!" Again I fell silent and studied, but it was beyond me. "Give me a hint."

"Un-uh... you've gotta get into it, man."

And so the week went. Each day they threw paint to paper; they slashed and they globbed, till I arrived to interpret their intent. To my constant amazement, they did have an explanation for everything! It reminded me of an Old West story I once heard. The government sent two Indian braves back east to attend a prestigious university. When they returned to their tribe after graduation, someone asked the old chief what he thought of the two young tribesmen. He said they could speak endlessly on any subject, but they didn't know how to do anything!

When I'd finished the Friday afternoon demonstration, I made one final trip around the class to say my goodbyes. I saved the two young collegiates in the corner until the end. I wanted to remember these two.

"Rich," I asked, "what are your plans next year after you graduate?"

"I dunno, man, guess I'll try to get a job."

"Aren't you going to follow your painting?"

"Naw, man, I don't want to prostitute my talent!"

"You're not going to continue painting?"

Rich looked down to his shuffling feet. "The way I see it, most artists don't become famous till late in life, so why not just wait till then to start painting!"

Shell-shocked by his logic and too late to argue, I shook his cold-fish hand and wished him good luck. Rich's shoulders were still bobbing and his feet still shuffling as I turned and stepped over to the ball-capped figure beside him.

John put down his brush and moved back from his easel so I could get a better view of his painting. I will always consider it a flaw in my analytical ability that here it was, Friday afternoon, and I had yet to uncork the hidden meaning of one of John's paintings without hints or help. This was my last chance. We both fell silent as I studied. The pressure was on! Finally I took a shot. "Greed?"

"Nope!"

"Anger?"

"Un-uh."

"Anything to do with astrology?"

"No, man, look at all that green!"

"You're Irish?"

"Naw, dude."

Finally I had to relent. "I give up!"

"Envy," he said.

Flustered, I stomped my foot. "Of course," I shouted, "how could I have missed that?"

"That's okay," John consoled me, "you were getting close."

"Yeah," I said, disgusted with myself. "But with all those green globs, I should have gotten that right away!"

John smiled as he pointed back to his green glob painting. "So, man, what do you think of it?"

After a week of jousting and arguing, I wanted to think John and I had found some common ground. I returned John's smile and answered him as honestly as I could. "Hey, man," I said, "it's far out!"

Egomania

When I was a young man in art school, I had the great, good fortune to be befriended by an older, wiser woman. Polly once told me, "The key to every man, is his ego." The thirty years since have led me to believe she was right.

"Hello? May I speak to Don Andrews please?"

"This is Don."

"Mr. Andrews, this is Nancy. It's such an honor to speak to you in person!"

"Please, Nancy, call me Don."

"Thank you, Don, you don't know me, but I'm your biggest fan. There are a lot of artists painting, teaching, and writing books these days, but I think you're way above the rest."

"Obviously, you're a person of discerning taste, Nancy. What may I do for you?"

"I'd like to sign up for your summer workshop on the coast of New Hampshire."

"Oh, Nancy, I'm sorry, but that's just six weeks away, and I'm afraid the class has been filled."

"Please don't tell me that, there's just no one who admires your work as much as I do. It is my dream to study with you. Isn't there some way you can work me in?"

"I hate to say it, Nancy, but there's a waiting list, and I'm afraid at this late date there's not much chance of you working up to the top."

"But I've been wanting to study with you for ages!"

"Nancy, I don't know what to say...perhaps we can work something out for next summer!"

"Mr. Andrews, please let me explain my situation. My daughter and I are planning a trip to the New England coast for the summer. I've been so excited, because it would be the perfect opportunity for me to take a workshop with you."

"Nancy, perhaps I have a solution. Since you're going to be on the New England coast this summer anyway, my friend, Skip Lawrence, will be teaching a workshop close by, on the coast of Maine. He's a gifted painter and teacher. I highly recommend him!"

"Oh," Nancy sighed... "I just got off the phone with Skip. He said his class has been filled for months. He told me to call you!"

Art, Politics and Religion

My plane touched down right on time; artists are always fascinated by the unusual. It was early summer in the desert, and the dry heat engulfed me. I like the desert, there's a vastness to it not found back east, and the Naples color-scheme is refreshing and uniquely beautiful. The desert is quiet, clean, and full of surprises; in Alabama, dogs are larger than rabbits.

As I came through the jet-way to my gate, I spotted a smiling lady of Rubinesque proportions holding a sign with my name on it. I approached and introduced myself. "Hi, I'm Don."

The lady grabbed her ample chest, inhaled with a snort, let out a giggle and exclaimed, "Oh, Mr. Andrews, I'm so happy to meet you," snort, snort, tee hee hee…

While we waited for my luggage, Sally filled me in on our class, local spots of interest, restaurants etc. I began to notice that at the beginning and end of each comment, Sally snorted, giggled or sighed, and often delivered some combination of all three. You might expect this from a happy person, had I said something amusing, but nothing we were discussing was funny.

I asked what time class started each morning. Sally smiled, grabbed her chest, snorted and said, "9:30," tee hee hee. I asked about the studio space. "Oh, we have plenty of room," snort, snort, giggle. To tell the truth, I consider myself a fairly humorous guy, so I began to anticipate Sally's reaction when I actually said something funny.

Once the baggage arrived and I had placed it in the car, Sally and I settled into a pleasant, if not down right jovial, conversation as we drove along. I caught myself leading our discussion in directions I knew would conclude with a punch line. When she asked my preference in models, I said, "My favorite model was one who showed up on time and had a pulse." This brought gasping inhalations, convulsive snorts, and peals of laughter. I had to contain my comic urges, for fear Sally would forget herself and drive off the road. But doggone, it was fun!

Looking back, I should have seen it coming, but I was having such a good time, the seriousness of her next question completely got by me.

Snort, giggle, ha ha ha, "So, Don, don't you get tired of staying in hotels all the time?"

"Do I! The only difference between a Holiday Inn and the Ramada is the color of the carpet!"

Sally blew a stitch at this, paused for a moment to catch her breath, and then exclaimed, "Oh, I knew it," snort, ha ha, "so I've taken the liberty of putting you up in a local bed and breakfast," tee hee hee!

"Oh?"

"Yes, I just know you'll love it!" Sally exclaimed, "and don't worry, you'll have plenty of privacy. You'll be the only guest! It's run by a really spry lady in her eighties, who I know you'll adore. She's such a dear, loads of personality and the house is oozing with charm," tee hee, snort. "You do like cats, don't you?"

Now the truth is, I do like cats, but all of a sudden something told me all was not right here. "I'm the only guest?"

"Yes," Sally snickered, "Cora can only take one guest at a time. Her house is rather small, quaint really. You won't believe how she has it decorated; you've never seen anything like it," snort snort, giggle...

Soon we turned off the interstate into a subdivision where walking after dark might be considered optional, past block after block of adobe houses. We turned again, the car slowed and Sally pulled into the driveway of a modest desert house, in the middle of a neighborhood block. Luggage in hand, I walked up to a front porch that was cluttered with hanging pots of dead plants, driftwood, and the kind of figurines you win at the county fair. Wind chimes jingled, wooden ducks with rotating wings oscillated in the breeze.

Sally rang the doorbell, turned to me and bubbled, "Don't you just adore this place?"

Across the street, two Mexican boys were working on a motorcycle in the front yard. Suddenly the door flew open and three huge cats darted past my feet. "Cleo, Roberto, Simon, come back here at once!" snapped the octogenarian. She then commanded, "Come," and we stepped into the house.

Cobwebbed paintings and photographs, once brightly colored western blankets, Mexican hats and cucarachas covered the walls. Shelves were cluttered with knick-knacks and bottles. Fake flowers and plastic birds in wire cages hung from ceiling beams. Books and stacks of magazines crowded the floor. Then I noticed the cats; Lord have mercy, cats were everywhere!

Sally gasped aloud, as her hands clamped in unison, one to my arm, and the other to her chest. "Oh, isn't this enchanting! I promised you it wasn't going to be the Holiday Inn, now didn't I?"

Cora reappeared in the doorway with one of the escaped felines; she gave Roberto an affectionate swat on the rear, and dropped him to the floor at my feet. Between giggles, Sally made introductions as the whine of a motorcycle rose from across the street.

Cora didn't smile as we were introduced. In fact, I thought I detected coldness in her glare. When I took her hand to shake, I was met with an impressive grip that served more warning than greeting. Meanwhile, Sally bubbled with excitement, "Oh, I'm so jealous," she exclaimed. "I can just imagine the stimulating conversation the two of you are going to have over breakfast." With that, Sally handed me her card, told me to give her a call if I needed anything, snorted, giggled, and made her exit.

Cora quickly closed the screen door behind Sally, spoiling Roberto's second attempt to escape. She turned to me with shoulders square, hands clasped behind her back. "You will have the bedroom on the left by the bath. Breakfast is at 7:30, if you smoke, go outside. Any questions?"

"No ma'am."

Then she added, "I have an important meeting to attend and will be leaving in less than an hour. Please see to it that my cats remain inside, should you go out."

I retreated to my bedroom, which measured 8 by 10 feet, and was decorated by the same interior designer who did the living room. On the single bed lay Roberto, my tabby roommate, who was obviously the permanent resident. After unpacking, I lay down beside him and we shared the same thought, escape!

The next morning at 7:30, I opened my door and stumbled out in search of breakfast. On the dining room table sat a lonesome bowl, a box of wheat germ and a glass of juice. No coffee! I could hear Cora in the kitchen as I removed a cat from my chair and took my seat. Cora entered from behind me, as silently as (if you'll excuse the expression) a cat, placed a single piece of toast on a napkin next to my bowl and took the chair opposite mine.

"Good morning, Cora," I said. "Aren't you going to have breakfast?"

"No, I fast during the morning hours."

"Oh, I see, so that's how you stay so slim?"

"Staying slim, as you put it, is not a concern, staying healthy is."

No doubt about it, Cora had a bone to pick, but at that moment I had a more urgent concern... "Uh, Cora, is there any coffee?"

Lines multiplied on her brow as she stated dryly, "No...no coffee in my house; coffee is an artificial stimulant that retards circulation. You will think far clearer today without it!"

Oh man, I couldn't believe this; in a little over an hour I was going to face a class of students, with unretarded circulation! I was pretty sure Cora could read the expression on my face. I was also pretty sure the smile of satisfaction on her face had little to do with my good health. I shifted my bloodshot gaze from Cora to the walls, which were covered with objects of every description. I focused on an unframed certificate and squinted to read it. "I see you're active with the Unitarian Church."

The sneer in her expression remained intact, but added to it came a genuine look of surprise. That's correct," she said. "Frankly, I'm a little shocked that you've heard of us."

"Why, yes, in fact I have good friends in my hometown who are quite active."

"Surely you're mistaken. I don't believe there are any chapters of our organization in your part of the country! I would imagine our concepts are a bit too open-minded for you people."

So much for cordial conversation! The hunt was on! Considering this was Monday morning, and I was scheduled to be here five days, I thought it best to diffuse the situation and win her over. That was my first mistake.

"Er…uh, well, I suppose it could be said that we in the south are a bit set in our ways. There's an old southern prayer that goes like this…Lord, please let me always be right, for I am hard to turn." All the while, I smiled my most disarming smile. I was pretty sure my gentle riposte would do the trick. That was my second mistake!

"Hard to turn indeed," she sniped. "More like backwards I'd say!"

In contrast to mine, Cora's eyes were alive and sparkling. I could see she had plans for breakfast after all!

"So, Cora, is the Unitarian church considered a religion?"

"The Unitarian church, is an organization to which I belong, it is not my religion. I am a Hopi Indian. Being a Hopi is a religion in and of itself. Our belief is pacifism, true pacifism."

Uh-oh…this conversation just took another left turn and here I sat caffeine free. Now, Don, I thought, just what are you going to say to that? I let a few moments pass in silence, hoping Cora would assume I was in deep contemplation, and then I replied, "Oh." Letting a few more moments pass, I followed up. "What exactly is true pacifism anyway?" Mistake number three…

Cora pinched her eyes between thumb and finger, then raised her head to focus on the heathen sitting before her. "Pacifism is a life in perfect balance with nature, the true way, the Hopi way." Then her eyes sharpened, "Which my fathers enjoyed until *your* people came!"

About then, I had this overwhelming urge to shout, "Circle the wagons!" but too late.

"The white man has disrupted everything in nature and all cultures. Your people have a loathsome desire to kill, even to the point of their own suicide; that's why you smoke and drink coffee! We Hopis would have created the perfect natural world, if not for the invasion of the white man."

Cora sat back to let me marinate in the knowledge of my sins. A cat bounded onto the table. I picked him up and returned him to his colleagues on the floor. Perhaps she was right; at that moment, I would have killed for a cup of coffee. Cora was deadly serious about all this, but something wasn't right. I focused my bleary eyes and took a good look at her. Cora certainly didn't look Indian to me. Her hazel eyes appeared to have a touch of cerulean. I braced myself.

"So, Cora, tell me, what descent are you?"

Cora jolted and I prepared for incoming. "I'm Hopi," she cried. "I was adopted by the tribal fathers over forty years ago! My heart, mind, and soul are guided by the natural laws of Hopi teachings, and I have lost all contact with my congenital self."

Okay, time to sound retreat. I took one more spoon full of wheat germ and gestured at my watch, "My, my, look at the time."

Sally didn't have to wait when she arrived to pick me up for class. Her eyes were as round as saucers. She gasped and clutched her chest as I entered the car. "Now, Don, I can't wait to hear," snort, "don't leave out a word," giggle, giggle, "not one word." Tee, hee, hee.

"Well, you said she was colorful. Do we have time to go by the drive-thru?"

That night, after a late dinner, Sally dropped me off at Cora's. All was dark and quiet as I slipped into the house. I had brought a little something with me for medicinal purposes, and thought the timing was about right. I crept into the kitchen, turned on the light, and opened the refrigerator to get a few cubes of ice. It's impossible to get ice out of a tray quietly but I thought I was doing a reasonable job. I then refilled and replaced the tray and closed the door. As I turned, there stood Cora like a statue.

"May I help you?"

"No thank you, Cora. I was getting some ice."

"For a drink?"

"Yes, ma'am."

"A drink of alcohol?"

"Just a nightcap, they say it's good for you."

She turned in a huff and disappeared in the shadows. From the darkness came her final word. "HA!"

Back in my room, I poured myself a drink and sat with my tabby roommate on our single bed. I began to browse through periodicals cluttering the nightstand. I'd never heard of *Alternative World* or *Mother Jones*. I casually leafed through a magazine. With a double take, I focused on the title of an article, "If Testosterone Is A Drug...Kick The Habit." I glanced down the page, where there was enlarged print of an excerpt from the article stating, "Castration Isn't Nuts!" I left that article and continued thumbing until my eye caught another title. "If He Wears The Pants, Don't Let Him In Yours!" Hair on the back of my neck bristled. The quiet of night was suddenly ominous. Rod Sterling's face popped into my mind. I checked the anatomy of my feline roommate and was relieved to find him still intact. Pacifism, my ass! I got up and locked the door.

The next morning at 7:29, I cracked open my bedroom door and peered out with one bloodshot eye. From my vantage point, I could only see my end of the table in the dining room. The bowl and box of wheat germ waited; all was quiet. On tiptoe, I entered the dining room and there sat Cora, like a Russian at a chessboard. Let the games begin!

"Good morning, Cora."

"Good morning."

I removed a cat from my chair and took a seat. I hadn't really looked outside to see, but in the Southwest, it's a pretty safe bet. "Looks like a beautiful day," I said.

"Perhaps," she replied. I could see her thoughts were elsewhere. Cora put her elbows on the table and unconsciously extended her index fingers to her lips and tapped, then her eyes locked on target. "Sally says you're an artist."

"Yes, that's right."

"What exactly do you paint?"

"I paint both figures and landscapes."

"What exactly, do you mean by figures?"

"People," I said, but I had a pretty good idea Cora knew exactly what I meant by figures. However, in my defense, just because a mouse doesn't think he can make it back to the burrow, doesn't mean he stops running!

"Women?"

"Yes, women."

"Naked women?"

"Yes, Cora."

"And you pay these women to sit in front of you naked!"

I tried to collect my uncaffinated thoughts. "To an artist, the human form is not only a thing of great beauty," I said, " but also the ultimate challenge of skill. If you were to paint a tree with the limbs too long, no one would notice. However, if you painted a figure with arms too long, even a child could see the mistake." My explanation was offered in all sincerity, but obviously this wasn't going to fly.

"And what do you do with these paintings of naked women?"

"Well, I sell them."

"People pay you money for these...these things?"

"Yes."

"Not only do you paint naked women, but you teach others to do so as well!"

It was more a statement than a question. I took a spoonful of wheat germ, enveloped toast in my napkin, and sprang to my feet. "Well, Cora, I don't want to be late for class."

"Ha!" she blasted.

Once again, after dinner that night, I returned to Cora's Bed & Breakfast. I sat with Roberto on our single bed and made up my mind. Enough was enough, thank you! My tabby roommate was about to get his side of the bed back. I searched my wallet and found the card Sally had given me upon my arrival. I hadn't paid any attention to it when she handed it to me, but now I read it. There was Sally's name and phone number, and printed below in bold pink letters, "The Giggle Gallery."

I picked up the receiver and dialed the number. After three rings an answering machine came on and Sally's lighthearted familiar voice, snorted, giggled, inhaled and sang, "Roses are red, violets are blue, if you leave a message, I'll get back to you," snort, giggle, tee hee hee! I replaced the receiver and leaned back on the bed. "Okay, one more night."

The next morning, I swung open my door right on time and strolled into the dining room. There's a certain freedom in total capitulation; I once saw a bumper sticker that read, "I feel better since I gave up."

The scene at the table was a duplicate of the past two mornings, wheat germ, no coffee, lots of cats, and Cora. I removed a cat from my chair and sat down. I gave Cora my impression of a smile, as she eyed me from her seat. I had to get through this, so I thought I'd try the high road one last time.

"Good morning, Cora," I began. "My goodness, you certainly have a house full of beautiful cats. You must love them!"

Cora gave me a wry smile. "Yes," she said, "the more people I'm around, the more I love cats." Yep, we were off and running!

"Well, they must be a handful. Have you ever considered having them spayed or neutered?" If you're keeping score on how many mistakes I've made with Cora, please add one here.

Cora's eyes flashed. "Fixed!" she roared. "You mean fixed?"

"Well...yes, Cora. I just thought..."

"That's just it," Cora interjected at the top of her lungs. "Everything you think, is out of keeping with nature. You think everything needs to be fixed!"

"Now wait a minute, Cora, I just thought this many cats might be a burden, and if money was a problem, there are local government agencies that can help you."

"Government help," she shrilled. "Your government has given quite enough help!"

For a moment, I thought Cora was going to have apoplexy. Bolts of lightning streaked across her eyes. Smoke jetted from flaring nostrils. She twitched and sputtered. A feline sprang from her lap as Cora catapulted from her chair, storming past me and out of the room, leaving behind one final word. "HA!"

Thirty minutes later, I stood out front waiting for my ride to arrive. How was I going to break this to Sally? I knew she had set up my stay at Cora's with the best of intentions. I just had to tell her straight out and that was that. Sally pulled into the drive, and I lowered myself into her car.

"Sally, we have to talk." She interrupted me with a whisper of a snort, a hint of a laugh, then exhaled and sighed.

"Don, I don't know quite how to tell you this, but I just got a call from Cora and I think it would be better to move you to a hotel. Cora says you're a very interesting young man, but your presence seems to be upsetting her cats!"

On Human Nature

My eyes were opened to the writer's art of studying human nature by my dear friend, C. Terry Cline. "It's their foibles and imperfections," Terry told me countless times, "that make the human species interesting!"

Terry and his wife Judy are my little older, much wiser writer friends, who to date have a dozen or more published suspense novels to their credit. They co-write their novels. One book Terry writes, and Judy edits, then they reverse roles and its Judy's turn to write, with Terry taking on the editing chore. It's great fun to sit with them in our little hometown restaurant as they discuss plot twists, character development, dialogue problems and resolutions. More than once, their discussion on the best way to murder some characters in one of their novels has been misconstrued by the couple in the next booth.

Terry is a master of language; words are his tools. You don't want to play Scrabble with him. Once, I made a five letter score with the word, *roast*. He countered off me with, *Zoroastrianism*. "I think it's a Persian religion," he said with an innocent smile, "but you're welcome to challenge."

No man ever loved a woman more than Terry loves Judy. He doesn't just love her, after all these years of marriage; he's still in love with her. It's a beautiful thing. Judy often joins us for our afternoon coffee break, and will leave a few minutes before us to get a bit of exercise, with a brisk walk back home. When Terry spots her strolling down the street, he'll slow down the car to match her pace. Elbow crooked out the window, he'll cruise along behind her, making catcalls and wolf whistles. Judy will try her best to ignore him, but when she can take it no longer, she'll turn with pointed finger and scold him like a schoolboy, but she can't help smiling while she's scolding.

Terry believes in the muses and has admiration and respect for all artists and all art forms. Over coffee, he will quote the poetry of A.E. Housman with one breath and admire Edward O. Wilson's definitive volume on the study of ants in the next. I know no other individual who sings the praises on a book about ants!

Ben Franklin once said, "A good man is worth ten good women, because he's ten times harder to find." My friend C. Terry Cline is that man. However, lest I be accused of painting half a portrait here, let me just say that C. Terry Cline has his mischievous side. In fact, the devil knows Terry well.

One Wednesday, as we sat in our booth having coffee, our waitress, Stella, came by with coffeepot in hand to top off our mugs. As she poured, Terry spoke up. "My goodness, Stella, is that a new dress you're wearing? It certainly is becoming!"

Stella is a dear lady, and has been a waitress at Julwin's Restaurant for as long as anyone can remember. She gave Terry a good-natured swat on the shoulder. "Terry," she blushed, "I've been wearing this rag for more years than I can count!"

I looked over to a faded print of sunflowers made more for comfort than style. Stella's rebuttal didn't slow Terry in the slightest.

"Well, it sure looks nice on you!" Stella swatted him again before she retreated, giggling.

"I'm gonna tell Judy," she warned. We fell back into conversation and I didn't give the incident another thought.

The next day was Thursday and once again as the day before, we sat talking in our booth when Stella came around for our refills. Terry interrupted himself. "Stella, are you doing your hair differently? It's positively striking!"

"Terry," Stella cooed, "I've been wearing my hair in this beehive for half my life!"

"Well," Terry shot back, "it's as stylish as anything I've seen in those Hollywood magazines!"

"Oh, Terry, you're a caution," she said as she turned and fluttered away. Again the incident flew right by me.

Friday afternoon found us haunting our usual booth. Judy joined us for lunch and when we'd finished our sandwiches, Stella came around to ask if we'd like dessert with our coffee.

"Stella, by chance did you make banana pudding today?" Terry asked, as if he didn't know Stella has made banana pudding at Julwin's restaurant every Friday for the past twenty years.

"Why yes, Terry, would you like a bowl?"

"Oh, Stella, I awoke this morning anticipating that you'd put your hand to that wonderful confection. I often wish I had the ability to write with the mystical flair you have for banana pudding. No doubt, I'd claim a Pulitzer!"

Judy and I took turns rolling our eyes. Shortly, Stella returned with a cereal bowl of banana pudding in each hand and placed one in front of Judy and the other in front of me.

"I'll be right back," she reassured Terry, and presently she returned with a gallon-mixing bowl, one third full of pudding, and set it down in front of Terry. "We had some extra," she said. "I hate for it to go to waste."

As Stella withdrew, Terry called out, "Stella, you're a master, an artist, it is an honor to place my feet beneath your table!"

For a moment, Judy and I sat in silence and visually compared our bowls to Terry's. "Judy," I asked, "is what's been going on what I think has been going on?"

Judy shook her head. "He's shameless," she said. Terry offered no defense. He didn't say a word, but between bites, he was smiling.

Time gets lost in our sleepy little town by the bay, and I can't say if it was the next month or the next year when my phone rang with Terry on the line. "Can you meet me for coffee?"

"Sure," I said, "Do you want me to pick you up?"

"No, I'm already here. Just come on up."

I washed out my paintbrushes and five minutes later I walked through the front door of Julwin's restaurant, to see Terry sitting with Sharon in our usual booth. Sharon is the public relations administrator for the Fairhope Chamber of Commerce. I pulled into the booth next to Terry, sitting across from the notebook and papers Sharon had before her on the table. Sharon is young and pretty, both Terry and I know her well. She's written slice of life articles on both of us for the local paper. Normally Sharon is upbeat and vivacious, but as I sat down I detected trouble looming behind her smile.

"Don," Terry asked, "you're not traveling the week of Easter are you?"

"No, I don't usually teach on holidays. Why do you ask?"

"Oh, no reason."

"So, Sharon," I asked, "how are you?"

"To tell you the truth," she said, "I have a problem."

"What's wrong?" I asked, but before she could answer, Terry interrupted.

"Sharon is in charge of our annual Easter Celebration, and with the holiday only three weeks away, she is trying to find someone to play the parts of Mr. McGregor and the Easter Rabbit for the festival."

"I see," I said, "so time is getting short."

Terry snapped a finger and pointed at Sharon. "I told you he'd grasp the urgency of the situation! The fact is," Terry continued, "to help Sharon out, I've agreed to play the part of Mr. McGregor. Now all she needs is someone with the self-confidence to play the part of the Easter Rabbit."

With that, Terry and Sharon fell silent, their eyes drifting around the room until in unison, they locked onto me. It took a moment to sink in.

"Oh No!"

"Now, Don," Terry urged, "hear us out before you rush to judgement. All we'll have to do is dress up a little and read a few stories to the kids, nothing to it. Besides, Sharon is desperate!"

I looked over at Sharon's pretty face, clouded with sadness. "I'm sorry," I said, "but you've got three weeks. I'm sure you'll find someone." The furl on Sharon's brow deepened with my rebuff.

"Don," Terry countered, "think of the children. You were a kid once weren't you? Remember the story of Mr. McGregor and the Easter Rabbit? What would Easter be without it? Besides, I thought you liked kids?"

"Of course I like kids, but…"

Terry cut me off. "I'd play the part of the rabbit and let you play the farmer, but he's supposed to be an old geezer, so I'm perfect for the part. All you'll have to do is wear a little rabbit make-up and sit there while I read the little tykes a story or two, and that's about it. We're appealing to your civic pride!"

I looked over to Sharon, her eyes yearning. "Please."

I massaged my temples. "Rabbit make-up?"

"Just a little," Terry assured me. "Nothing compared to me. I'll be wearing overalls, straw-hat, a cane, and pipe. We'll look foolish but it'll be great fun."

"Whiskers, I suppose?"

"A few, not many," Sharon promised. "Whatever feels right?"

"How long will this take?"

"Thirty minutes, an hour tops,"Terry promised. "It'll be over before you know it, and we'll have a memory to cherish forever. What do you say?"

Again our booth fell silent as I drew a long breath. "You're sure about this Terry?"

"Absolutely!"

Terry and Sharon leaned forward in anticipation. I exhaled and shook my head. "Okay," I said. "I'll do it for the children."

With that, the storm clouds broke from Sharon's face. Terry put his arm around my shoulder and gave me a hug. Sharon gathered her papers, and popped up, as if she were spring-loaded. Blowing us both a kiss, she proclaimed, "You two are the sweetest men in this town!" Then pointing to her watch, "I'm late for a meeting." Sharon took two steps before she hesitated and spun back to me.

"Don, I'll have someone deliver the rabbit costume to your house this week, in case alterations are needed."

"Rabbit costume!" I stammered. "Nobody said anything about a costume!"

"Well, you do have to look like a rabbit, but don't worry, we'll pick it up after the parade."

"Parade? What parade?"

"Now, now," Terry consoled, "It's just a few blocks. You know we have an Easter parade every year."

I turned in time to catch a glimpse of Sharon, as she rounded the front door. Again I turned to Terry.

"Don't worry," he said, "we'll have a great time!" But he was smiling as he spoke, and I'd seen that smile before. It was the same smile he had over that bowl of banana pudding!

I didn't realize the depths of the snare in which I'd been trapped, until the following week when a large package arrived at my door. When I finally got up the nerve to open it, my worst fears were realized. Slowly, I reached down and pulled out a fluffy white jumpsuit bunny costume, complete with pink stomach and a snowball cottontail. There was a hood-like headpiece attached with foot long ears, so top-heavy that when I pulled the hood on, the ears hung off the back side of my head in odd directions. The costume included footwear that resembled giant dome-shaped white slippers, the size of scuba fins. When I put them on, I discovered I had to raise my feet to my knees in order to take a step. To make matters worse, the whole thing fit me like a glove.

As I stood staring at myself in the mirror, one thought occupied my mind. "No matter how long it takes, Terry, I'm gonna get even with you!"

I lived in a state of denial for the next two weeks, but soon the fateful day was upon me. That Saturday morning, I peered out my window to unanswered prayers. Bees buzzed azaleas as they boasted pink blossoms, the bay breeze blew soft and scented, and not one cloud challenged the sun as it rose to announce a picture perfect spring morning.

Terry and I had agreed that he'd pick me up for the short drive to the elementary school gymnasium, where the festivities were to commence. Terry pulled into my drive right on time and honked the horn. With knee high steps, I clop, clop, clopped, out to his waiting car. Terry sat looking ridiculous in farmer's overalls and straw-hat. Freckles were painted on his nose and a corncob pipe dangled from the corner of his mouth. It took me a minute to open the car door with my paw mitts and then I had to turn and back myself into the front seat.

"Hold on," Terry shouted as I sat down. "You're bending your ears!" I had to fold the enormous rabbit feet back one at a time to get them onto the floorboard. I situated myself before turning to Terry. White pasty make-up and whiskers covered my face.

For a moment there was silence. Terry's eyes glistened and the pipe in his mouth twitched, as he struggled to keep a straight face. Then the dam broke and the car erupted as we both burst out laughing. "You know," Terry pointed his pipe at me, "I always thought you looked good in white!"

We were greeted at the gymnasium by a throng of children. They weren't overly impressed with Terry, not sure who he was or what his role would be, but me they loved! Instantly, I was surrounded by waves of pre-schoolers, reaching out to touch and feel me. Terry was led to a large wicker rocking chair, where he sat to read the story of Mr. McGregor and the Easter bunny. I took my place on the floor with the children. A small curly-haired girl inched her way up to me, then waved to her friends. Within seconds, I was smothered beneath a mound of squealing, crawling, miniature humans. There we sat while Terry bellowed prose with unbridled flair. A storybook in one hand, his corncob pipe fanning the air with the other, he recounted the age-old tale at the top of his lungs to the delight of the awe-struck children.

When Terry finished the story of Mr. McGregor chasing the Easter Rabbit from his garden, we rose and said our good-byes to our wide-eyed audience. Presently, we were led back out to the street in front of the school, where lines of a procession were forming. There were police cars, fire trucks and the high school band. Children in pink and blue Easter dresses and bonnets were shepherded into place. The centerpiece for the procession was a tractor drawn flatbed trailer, elaborately decorated in papier-mâché. The floor of the trailer bed was made up like rows of a vegetable garden. Overhead was a flower-covered sign that read, "Mr. McGregor and the Easter Bunny."

While being helped up on the trailer, I was thankful we lived in a small town. However, from my new vantage point, judging from the look of the assembled crowd mulling along Main Street, it appeared that the local population was in perfect attendance.

When we had all taken our position the lead police car sounded its siren, the fire truck honked its bullhorn, and the band marched in place. Our tractor rumbled to life in a cloud of blue exhaust. Ahead, the crowd drew close. With a jolt, we lurched forward and slowly, oh so excruciatingly slowly, we began to roll.

Inching down Main Street, relentless clouds of exhaust flowed from the tractor. Countless people with children on their shoulders waved and screamed at me as our float lumbered by.

Terry was like a caged bird on a weekend pass. He laughed and waved back to the masses, then he'd chase me around the papier-mâché garden, whacking me on my backside with his cane, and then he'd laugh and wave some more. I tried my best to get away from him, but my giant footgear caught in the paper vegetables, hampering my retreat. The good news was, our Easter parade only traveled five or six blocks. The bad news was, we were proceeding at two miles an hour, Terry laughing, waving and chasing me with his cane every inch of the way.

It was quite a day! An eternity later, I stood alone scrubbing the make-up and whiskers from my face. I stared into the mirror and repeated an earlier vow. "No matter how long it takes Terry…"

You can never really repay a man who talks you into wearing a rabbit suit on the Main Street of your hometown. I was once a respected member of my community. I paid my taxes and made charitable contributions. I've written books and magazine articles on painting, I've sat on juries for regional and national art competitions. I have legitimate reasons to demand a fair amount of respect and dignity in my hometown, but I can attest to this fact. No one ever looks at you quite the same after they've seen you in a rabbit suit. I can't explain the difference; it's just different. Your life is forever divided into before and after. Unless you've actually experienced the feelings that accompany dangling ears, a bobbing cottontail and floppy feet, you cannot appreciate my desire for revenge.

As so often happens in life, some weeks later, I was given the gift of an opportunity. It was like spotting a gold coin, lying bright and shiny on a virgin beach. From out of nowhere, here was my chance and I seized it!

Terry and I had finished our coffee and ambled up to the cash register by the restaurant front door. We waited our turn to pay the bill behind a well-dressed, diamond and pearl laden lady in her early forties, who was talking to the owner, Cathy, across the counter. Cathy paused and looked over to Terry.

"Terry, is there a taxi service in this town?"

Terry stepped forward and responded pleasantly, "No, there isn't," and then he turned to face the attractive lady and added, "If I may be of service, I'll be glad to give you a ride wherever you'd like to go."

Beautiful women are cautious by nature and the lady was obviously a stranger in town. She gave Terry an expression of uncertain thanks and then paused to more carefully size him up. Terry, seeing the lady's hesitation, nodded chivalrously, and tried to reassure her.

"Allow me to introduce myself, I'm C. Terry Cline, a local author, and my friend here is artist, Don Andrews. I'm sure he'll be glad to vouch for me!"

For the first time the lady turned to me searching for affirmation, and there it was, so perfect, so simple, so clear. I looked down earnestly and lowered my voice for dramatic emphasis.

"Miss, I wouldn't let him get the door shut on you!"

She jumped back as if I'd pulled a knife! Terry's face registered a question mark of bewilderment until his eyes met mine and my long awaited chance for revenge betrayed me to him. Instantly aware of the situation he'd boxed himself into, he bowed over in laughter, one hand across his stomach, the other hand holding the counter for support.

"Well, miss," I offered soberly, "he has been doing some better with that new medication!" The poor lady's eyes popped wide as saucers.

"My word!" she exclaimed, recoiling still further.

Terry was momentarily defenseless, but I knew this window of opportunity would close quickly. I felt I had time to extract one more pound of flesh. "Terry, how long have you been out on parole now anyway?"

With that, the lady clutched her bag to her chest and bolted by us for the door.

This had been great fun and I longed to savor the moment, but the joke was over. I ran after the poor lady to apologize. I stopped her with her hand on the front door and explained that I was playing a joke on my friend, to even an old score. I offered the most glowing biographies on both Terry and myself. We were artists, saints, and pillars of the community. Finally her expression softened as I bombarded her with our accolades. She settled as I soothed her, she listened as I apologized, she even nodded and thanked Terry for his offer, but she never did take that ride.

Edenton

Edenton, North Carolina is one of those disappearing treasures the super-slide crowd hasn't discovered yet. It is perched on the shore of the Chowan River, just before it flows past the Outer Banks into the Atlantic Ocean. People from Edenton still speak and wave greetings on the streets, and you can walk to the river from anywhere in town in five minutes.

It's a pleasure to read the crime report in the local bi-weekly paper. "Last night someone stole the tools out of old Mr. Crenshaw's truck..." Then three days later they have to print a retraction, because he found them!

The pirate, Blackbeard, caused a little trouble in the area some time back but things have settled down nicely.

The North Carolina Watercolor Society had invited me to Edenton in conjunction with their yearly show. The society holds its annual event in a different town in North Carolina each year, and I was told this was "high cotton" for Edenton.

The week had gotten off to a frantic start. I judged the show on Saturday and had dinner with the society officers. Sunday I did a demonstration at the annual meeting and attended the dinner banquet that night. Monday I taught class and was invited to dinner with the workshop director, Ann, and her husband, Dr. Richard Hines.

Ann dropped me at my hotel after class and said she'd be busy in the kitchen, so Richard would pick me up for our dinner date.

Two hours later, Richard pulled up in a snazzy new red pick-up truck. I commented on it as I got in and he beamed, the way only a man can beam about owning a truck!

"I've just had it a few days," he grinned, "and it's already gotten me in trouble."

"What happened?"

"Edenton's such a quiet little town," Richard said, "we only have one police officer working the night shift during the week. Bill's a fine fellow and he's going to do well on the force, but he's young and over-anxious. We live in a townhouse in the historic district. There's no parking on our street, but the police allow the homeowners to park there anyway because none of the houses have driveways. A few days ago, I traded my car for this truck and that night I parked it in my usual spot. The next morning I had a parking ticket on my windshield. The city needs the money, so I went ahead and mailed in the fine."

"Last night I was sitting on my front porch when Bill came by in the cruiser. I waved him down and told him the truck he had ticketed was mine. He begged me to give it back to him, but I told him it was too late, I'd already paid the fine. I thought we'd have a good laugh, but Bill was embarrassed and apologetic, so to make him feel better, I said, 'Okay, you owe me one!'"

"That would only happen in a small town like Edenton," I said.

"Yep," Richard agreed, "there's nothing like living in a small town!"

The following day after class, Ann dropped me off at my hotel, and like a true southern lady, again offered dinner. I thanked her for her hospitality, but declined in favor of a quiet night to catch my breath.

After dining, back in my hotel room, there wasn't much on television. I decided to walk a few blocks down to the river to stretch my legs and enjoy the evening air. I fixed myself a drink, and changed from dinner clothes to a more comfortable T-shirt, shorts and flip-flops.

A few blocks later, I sat on a park picnic table overlooking the serenity of the Chowan River. The warm September air was a soothing balm. An orange cat jumped up on my table, and meowed a greeting. He eyed me cautiously for a moment as I reached out to offer a scratch, then his tail sprang up and he sidestepped until he got within rubbing range.

Far off, above the tree line, dark rumbles and flashes delivered the evening forecast. No need to hurry off though, the clouds were hours away. Things move slowly here.

Mesmerized by the river view and late summer twilight, I didn't notice the sounds of a car slowly pulling up behind me.

"Good evening sir," a voice called out.

Like I said, people are still friendly in this forgotten little haven.

"Good evening," I replied.

I turned to see a smartly dressed policeman getting out of his black and white cruiser, ten feet behind me.

"Enjoying the sunset?" he asked in a lazy southern drawl, much like my own.

"It's great."

He took a few steps toward me and I dare say it wasn't until that moment that it dawned on me; this might not be a social call.

"Mind if I ask what you have in that plastic cup?"

"Plastic cup?" I blinked as I looked down at the clear plastic hotel cup sitting by my side, filled with straight vodka on the rocks.

Stepping up next to me, he pointed a finger at the cup, gesturing a silent request for me to identify the clear liquid contents.

"Uhhh…it's mostly ice," I said, a sheepish grin plastered across my face.

"Mind if I see for myself?"

There was no reaction as the officer raised the cup to his nose and sniffed above the rim.

Oh, good, I thought, maybe he'll think it's water. I'll bet the ice has melted some!

Then in slow motion, he crooked his elbow as if it were in a cast, bringing the cup to his pursed lips and ever so gently, took a sip. Wincing, and spewing, he jerked the cup away!

"What is that stuff?" he gasped.

Just then, my fair-weather orange friend sprang down from the table, did a figure eight around the officers' legs, meowed an explanation that we were not together, and briskly strolled away.

"May I see some identification please?"

Heart pounding like a piston, I reached into the empty hip pocket of my shorts.

"Ha, ha, officer, you won't believe this, but I left my wallet in my pants pocket when I changed clothes back at the hotel."

The pathetic smile I'd been offering began to quiver around the edges while his glare grew steadily more stoic!

"Sir, are you aware of the city ordinance prohibiting possession of alcoholic beverages on public property?"

"Well…of course, officer, I mean without a doubt there uhh…"

"Sir, are you also aware of the vagrancy statutes in this county that require all citizens above the age of eighteen to possess at least two approved pieces of personal identification?"

"Uhh…two you say?"

"Sir, are you here in a motor vehicle?"

"No, officer…if you'll give me a minute, I can explain everything!"

He looked me square in the eyes as he crossed his arms on his chest.

"I was just…uh…enjoying the air, so I thought I'd take a walk. You can give me the test, I'll be glad to walk the line…I mean I can touch my nose, see?"

Slowly the officer shook his head. "You're not from around here are you?"

"No sir, I'm from New Hampshire."

A suspicious brow arched. "You don't sound like you're from New Hampshire."

"No, no….ha, no of course I don't. I'm from Alabama; but now, I live in New Hampshire, at the moment see, is what I mean!"

"Sir, may I ask what exactly is your business in Edenton?"

"I'm here with the North Carolina Watercolor Society, to judge their annual show and teach a painting workshop."

"A what?" his face screwed up with the question.

"I…uh teach painting, art that is."

"Is there anyone in town who can verify any of this?"

"Yes sir, officer, of course there is…ha ha…let's see, uh…Ann. Ann and Dr. Hines."

"I don't suppose you have their number?"

"Uhh…no officer, I mean, yes I do have their number, but it's in my wallet, which I don't have now…no…no sir!"

"Sir, would you step over to the car please?"

He opened the door of the cruiser, reached in and pulled out the radio microphone, punched a few buttons on the transmitter and spoke into the mike.

"Flo, can you connect me to the Hines' residence," giving the operator the street address. Eyeing me all the while, as if any second I might take a cue from my orange feline friend and make a run for it, he finally spoke into the microphone.

"Dr. Hines, sorry to bother you, yes of course, you too…"

Standing there, I couldn't help but think how this was going to look on the front page of the North Carolina Watercolor Society Newsletter. "Watercolorist, Don Andrews, served as this year's exhibition juror and did a painting demonstration at the opening reception. He also taught a workshop for the group. Unfortunately, the class was cut short due to Mr. Andrews being arrested for vagrancy and public drinking!"

I tried my best to grasp the gist of the ongoing conversation. The officer paused to look me up and down.

"He's tall, thin, not much of a dresser…"

Then his face softened, he laughed, apologized again for the inconvenience, and replaced the radio mike.

"Mr. Andrews, I'm going to let you go if you'll promise to pour out that drink, and walk directly back to your hotel."

"Right away, officer."

Guilt, instantly replaced with embarrassment, I couldn't help but ask.

"Officer, did you talk to Dr. Hines?"

"Yes, he vouched for you."

"Uh…if you don't mind my asking, exactly what did Dr. Hines say?"

The young officer gave me a crooked smile.

"He said, 'We're even for the parking ticket on his truck!'"

Four Stars

Hotel chains spend millions of dollars promoting how they are special or different, but when it comes right down to it, the difference between one hotel and another is the color of the carpet. From four star to economy, a hotel room consists of a bed, a bathroom, phone, TV, and a window overlooking the hotel parking lot.

Once I was hired by a non-profit museum that wanted our painting workshop to just break even on their books, so the director put me up in an exotic four-star hotel. The lobby of the hotel was a giant atrium, alive with the sounds of water flowing from waterfalls, framed by a forest of tropical plants. Ornate chandeliers illuminated the polished mahogany front desk. The bellboy knew my name when he delivered my luggage to my room. It cost me three dollars, but he knew my name. After he put my bags down on the plush carpet, collected his tip and left, I took a moment to survey my domain.   There was a bed, a bathroom, phone, and TV.   I walked over to the window and drew back the chintz curtains.   Sure enough, three floors below was the hotel parking lot.

That evening, I had an early dinner in the hotel restaurant and rode the glass bubble elevator back up to my floor.   As we ascended, the view of the tropical garden lobby became more and more impressive.   Tiny lights illuminated the palm trees and fountains, and a musician played a grand piano by an open bar.

It's the little things, I thought to myself as I stood silently soaking up the view.   Mahogany desks, chandeliers, tropical flowers and waterfalls!   I think this high living agrees with me!

It was still early when I got back to my room, so I thought I'd get comfortable and enjoy a lazy evening watching TV.   I put on a favorite old T-shirt and my wooly black jogging pants, which are a magnet for the fur from our three light-haired dogs.   Martha washes them relentlessly, but it seems the dog fur becomes more and more embedded.   I tell her to think of my jogging pants as mohair with character.

I made a pyramid of pillows against the headboard, sat back, and began clicking through the 99 channels on the remote control.   On channel 97 I came upon "Liberty Valance", one of my all time favorite John Wayne classics. I set down the remote control and settled in for the evening. Five minutes before John Wayne and Lee Marvin almost slap leather, because Lee Marvin tripped Jimmy Stewart, I decided to make a quick run down the hall to the snack machines.

I grabbed my wallet and double-checked to make sure it contained my room card key. I opted not to worry about socks and shoes; the carpet was thick, and the halls were quiet. Clad in T-shirt and dog-fur jogging pants, I sprinted down the hall to a small room filled with vending machines. Quickly, I loaded both hands and pockets with bags of junk food, turned and retraced my barefoot steps back to my room.

At my door, I cradled the bags of carbohydrates in one arm while I fished my card key from my pocket with the other. I produced the plastic key and inserted it in the door lock, expecting the little light to blink green signifying entry, but to my dismay it blinked red. After a few attempts, I set my bags of empty calories down and more carefully entered the card into the lock, but still the red light blinked. I tried inserting it slowly, quickly, backwards, forwards, upside down and right side up, but no matter what I tried, the red light denied me access.

Unfortunately, I was familiar with this particular problem. It's happened to me several times over the years, and there is only one solution. The plastic card key works by way of a magnetic code programmed when you receive your key upon arrival. When the card becomes demagnetized, the only solution is to have the card reprogrammed at the front desk. Time was suddenly of the essence.

Agitated, I retrieved my junk food, filled both pockets till they bulged out like giant chipmunk cheeks and sprang down the cushy carpet to the elevator. I pushed the down button. Presently a bell rang and the door to the glass bubble elevator peeled open. I entered in such haste, I practically ran over the handsome middle-aged couple standing there. She was elegant in her high heels and satin evening gown. Her hair was pushed off her neck to accentuate diamond earrings. He was decked out in black tie and dinner jacket, his silver gray hair combed in a pompadour as polished as the shine on his shoes. I gave them a sheepish smile; they nodded mutely and stepped away from me. He rolled his eyes and winked at her, she returned a pout and clutched the arm of his jacket. The elevator door closed and slowly we began to descend.

An hour before, the lobby had been deserted, but from my vantage point I could see a swirl of activity as throngs of well-dressed, beautiful people milled about below. Then I looked up, and in doing so, I caught my own reflection in the glass elevator. Aside from being barefoot, I had a bag of cookies hanging from my bulging left pocket, a bag of corn chips dangled from the right, my T-shirt hung out from behind. Worse still, the hair on the right side of my head was sticking out like a wing. Hoping to escape their notice, I casually turned from my elegant riding companions and jammed my T-shirt back into my jogging pants. Simultaneously, I licked a palm and tried to slick down the bird's nest growing out of the side of my head. My preening had just begun when a bell rang and the elevator doors opened to the entrance of the lobby.

I made a hasty exit, stepping out on a marble floor as cold as a sheet of New England ice. Dodging beautiful people, I hopped up to an attractive young lady standing behind the front desk. She wore a bow tie, white starched shirt and suspenders. She gave me a puzzled look and asked dryly if she could be of help. When I explained my problem, she offered a perfunctory apology, and took my card-key from me. Placing the plastic card in a little black box, she punched a few buttons, retrieved the card from the box and handed it back. I grabbed the card, thanked her, and quickly made my retreat.

Dancing on frozen feet back to the elevator entrance, I pushed the up button and waited for the doors to open. As I stood there, two attractive older couples came up to wait beside me. When the bubble elevator finally arrived, I jumped in, pushed my floor number, and then turned to the two couples still standing outside the doorway.

"Going up?"

"You go ahead," one gentleman sputtered. "We'll catch the next one."

Ascending, I had time to calculate that I had missed the aforementioned steakhouse scene, but with any luck, I could still catch my favorite scene of all. It's the one where Liberty has been shot, and is lying in the street in front of a saloon. A crowd gathers, and the town doctor is summoned. Presently, the top-hatted physician staggers out of the bar, cuts through the crowd, takes one look at Liberty and calls out his prescription of "Whisky, quick!" Someone hands the doctor a bottle, he pulls the cork, turns the bottle up, taking a hefty snort, looks down at Liberty and declares, "He's dead!" They don't make movies like that anymore! My calamity behind me, my mood rebounded with anticipation.

I exited the bubble like a track star and dashed down the hall to my door. Pulling the plastic key from my pocket, I inserted it and watched in disbelief as the little light on the lock blinked red. Filled with frustration, I grabbed the door handle and shook it. Then I tried the card again and again in every imaginable combination, but to my dismay the red light vetoed my entry.

"Damn," I cursed, cookies crunching as I jammed the key back into my pants pocket. Down the plush carpet hall I raced, hoping the elevator was still waiting at my floor. To my chagrin, the numbers over the elevator door indicated the bubble was four floors above me and headed in the wrong direction. As I stood there stewing, I tried to estimate if the elevator and lobby time ahead of me would overlap the time left before the upcoming movie scene. If everything went off without a hitch, I figured, I might still make it, but it was going to be close!

When the elevator returned to my floor it hadn't taken more than two or three minutes, but Einstein's theory on time relativity was coming into play. Alone I stood muttering obscenities, unconsciously raking my toes through the expensive carpet. I watched as the numerals above the elevator door climbed up to nine, stopped and slowly returned to three. Finally, a bell chimed announcing its return and the doors crept open. I vaulted into the bubble! Three teenage debutants standing inside jumped back as if they'd seen a mugger! Their smiling chatter instantly evaporated as, in unison, they turned their backs to me and clustered in the far corner. I pushed the lobby button and at a snail's pace we began our descent. From out of nowhere, the silence was broken by a smirk, then came a snort and a giggle. Holding back snickers, the three girls vibrated till, finally, they all burst out laughing! Mercifully, we soon reached the lobby and I shot through the doorway as soon as it opened enough for me to pass.

Wide-eyed, the night clerk watched me as I scurried, once again, across the icy marble floor. I handed her my key and stood there smoldering as she again punched the magnetized code into the plastic. She returned my key with a more genuine apology for my trouble.

"Look," I growled, holding the key up like a knife, "I'm getting tired of riding up and down in that elevator barefoot! What do I do if this card doesn't work?"

"Mr. Andrews," she reassured me, "I'm positive your key is properly coded this time. But if there's any problem, don't bother coming back down to the lobby. There's a phone in the elevator; just call from there and we'll send maintenance up to your room."

"All right," I nodded to her, turned, and skated back across the refrigerated floor. I ran up beside two stylish ladies as they stood by the elevator entrance. When the doors opened I entered but they held their places silently frowning at each other. "Going up ladies?"

"Uhhh, you go ahead," one lady said. "We'll just wait for our husbands."

I punched my floor number, the doors closed, and alone I ascended. "I just might make it yet," I encouraged myself as the elevator slowed to my floor. Adrenaline pumping, I bolted down the hall to my door, grabbed the key from my pocket and thrust it into the lock. My heart sank as the red light greeted me once again. Fuming with frustration, I turned and stormed up the hall to the elevator to make my call. I stalked the elevator entrance, barking and cursing till, finally, the door opened on my floor. The horrified young couple inside didn't argue when I explained to them that I wasn't going down, I just needed to use the phone. I reached over to a little door handle marked phone, pulled it open and snatched up the receiver, but I didn't make the call. I couldn't. The elevator phone was out of order!

Chemistry

No two workshop groups are the same. Like a soup comprised of so many ingredients, each class takes on its own unique flavor. Some are more industrious, some competitive, some more friendly and relaxed, but there was one class I remember, that was something else!

A few summers back, I was scheduled to teach at the Greenville Arms 1889 Inn in the Hudson River Valley of central New York. I had spent the week before on vacation with Martha and the kids at her parents' summer camp on Lake Ontario. All the sun, fun, food and recreation had taken its toll on me, and, as the day of departure approached, I was secretly dreading getting back to work.

Greenville is just off Route 90 on the way from Lake Ontario to our home in New Hampshire, so Martha and the kids dropped me off that Sunday afternoon. We said our goodbyes and away they drove. Wistfully, I watched and waved as our van pulled away.

Eliot, the owner of the Greenville Arms and workshop director, showed me to my room. He told me I was scheduled to meet my class at six o'clock for a get-acquainted dinner. I had about two hours to settle in, clean up and dress for the evening.

As I unpacked my things, I couldn't help feeling a little sorry for myself. Why hadn't I studied to become a doctor, instead of trying to make a living with my limited art ability. It was only yesterday that I lay on the beach with Martha and the kids, not a care in the world, and now I found myself about to meet a group of strangers who paid good money to listen to my ramblings. I didn't know who to feel sorrier for, them or me. Eliot said we had a small group consisting of eight day-students driving in for the class each day, and six students staying at the Arms with me. All six had arrived and would be present for dinner. Yes, poor pitiful me! If not for the years of concentrated effort, demands for high scholarship, and the cost, I could have been a doctor, I just knew it!

I opened the screen door to the foyer of the stately Victorian house. Ornate woodwork gave silent testimony to an age of craftsmanship long gone by. I proceeded into the dining room where six well-dressed, distinguished-looking people sat talking amiably among themselves. There were two men and four women. I introduced myself and we soon settled into the usual patter, otherwise known as *making nice*.

Kate and Veronica were university art professors; Claire was a high school art teacher. Mona was a retired illustrator from New York City. Both Paul and Harold were practicing architects. All were well into their middle years except Mona, who was a little older. Before dinner our server came by to offer wine, which Mona declined in favor of a double vodka martini. For a while everything progressed smoothly until Mona turned to Kate and spoke in a scorched gravelly voice.

"Forgive me for saying so, but it is my opinion that the art departments in our educational system are a leading factor in the lack of competence now prevalent in the New York art scene!"

"Uh-oh," I thought, "so much for making nice!" Whether Mona's views were valid or not, three of the six people at our table were involved in the art education system at some level. Kate put down her wine glass and turned to Mona.

"I don't take offense to your statement, nor do I totally disagree with it, but consider what we're up against in art education these days. Student-teacher ratios are up, material costs are through the roof. Without exception, the art departments in high school and university systems across the country are put last on administrative lists, except when the topic turns to funding cuts!"

"That's true," Veronica added, "and also consider that college kids are just kids. They love to play artist, but behind the posturing and sophisticated jargon, they don't get serious about art until they've had a taste of the real world. In fact, one of the reasons I'm here is to discuss art with people who can think of something other than who they're going to sleep with on Saturday night!

"Oh, shoot," Claire blurted out from the other end of the table, "and I thought we were going to be friends!"

There was a moment's hesitation, then the table erupted in laughter!

Disaster averted, ice broken, the conversation bobbed about the table, sometimes serious and arresting but salted with a vein of sarcasm and wit. Several times over dinner, the conversation turned to education.

"I was a math major in college," Paul said. "I'd always been interested in art so I took an art history course to satisfy my curiosity. The class met once a week for an hour. We began the semester studying caveman petroglyphs and finished up the class with modern art. I caught the flu and missed a class one week, so I asked a friend what material had been covered and he said, 'Something called the Renaissance!'"

"Most of my art education has been on my own as well," Harold said. "The closest we got to studying art in the architecture department at Ohio State, was the difference between Roman and Greek architraves and colonnades. I'm sure some people get excited about that kind of thing, but it was a little hard to warm up to!"

"Wait a minute," Paul shot back, "I thought Roman and Gothic reliefs were pretty racy! Just think of all those changes in weight distributions on octagonal columns a hundred feet above your head!" As if mesmerized, Paul lifted his eyes to the ceiling and softly exclaimed, "Weight ratios!"

I watched Mona from the corner of my eye. Now on her second double, she listened intently, but her expression was sour and she had yet to join in.

"So, Mona," I asked, "what are your painting goals this week?"

She took a pull from her double as the table fell silent. "I would like to work larger and more interpretational. After forty years of illustration, I want to loosen up."

"I can't speak for anyone else," Harold mused, "but after thirty years of architectural rendering, I feel the need to tighten up!"

And so the evening went. These people were intelligent, professional and serious about painting, but they all had a touch of mischief and this was the first night of a week long awaited. All around the table everyone was laughing; everyone except Mona.

Monday morning class convened in the carriage house art studio behind the main house. Just before nine o'clock our eight day-students arrived, introductions were made, and we all got down to business.

After my morning lesson, the group dispersed to begin their paintings. I bided my time before walking around the room to offer suggestions and answer questions. Mona didn't acknowledge me as I approached her. She was crouched over a quarter sheet painting, just under way.

"I thought you wanted to work larger this week," I said.

Mona shrugged her shoulders without looking up. "I'm not ready yet." She was working from a reference photograph of the misty Maine coastline. Fog meshed with jagged rocks to create an ethereal mood. I picked up the photograph to study it more closely.

"Did you take this?"

"Yes," she snapped, "what's wrong with it?"

"Nothing, Mona, the reflected light is striking."

"It's mostly pollution," she said.

When four o'clock rolled around, the eight day-students washed out their brushes, said their goodbyes, and scurried off to their homes and families, leaving the six and me at our easels. One of the advantages of a workshop at the Greenville Arms is that you can continue to work in the studio after class, but the atmosphere is more casual.

Shortly, Eliot showed up to ask if anyone would like coffee.

"What I'd really like," Mona blurted out, "is a double martini."

"I've got a bottle of wine," Veronica offered, "but it won't go around."

Harold asked Eliot if there was a liquor store in town and everyone quickly made an order.

"Eliot," Claire said, "forget the coffee. What we need is some ice!"

We worked until six o'clock, took a few minutes to clean up and rendezvoused at our usual table for dinner.

Pulling back cushioned chairs, we took our seats in unison. The ladies surrounded Mona at the other end of the table.

"I thought you were going to work larger?" Kate asked Mona.

"All my papers have been cut down to quarter sheets!"

"I've got a quire of Arches in my room," Veronica said. "You're welcome to all you need."

"Thank you, but I don't have brushes large enough to handle a full sheet anyway."

"I've got more brushes than Cheap Joe," Claire offered, "just help yourself."

"Well," Mona hesitated, "I'm just not ready."

"Come on, Mona," Kate said, "if we girls waited till we were ready, we'd still be virgins!"

Mona stared into her martini glass. "Okay, tonight I'll try one!"

"I know just how you feel," Paul consoled her. "Painting out of your comfort zone in a workshop is scary. For thirty years I've been paid big bucks to be exact with edges of lines, and today Don tells me to start by painting through them!"

"We've all been taught to be exact when we paint," Claire said, "because the public sees precision as a criterion for good painting."

"I know I'm too tight, and I get no pleasure from painting details for their own sake," Paul said, "but that's what my gallery wants, that's what sells. It's true, I don't have to make a living with my art…"

"Be thankful for that," Harold interrupted.

Paul laughed. "Okay, but I do like to sell, don't you? Don't we all?"

"Selling aside," Kate said, "I want my painting to be subject oriented, and creative as well. Why does creativity always refer to non-objective painting? Can't landscape painting be creative?"

"For that matter, why is non-objective painting automatically described as creative?" Harold said. "It seems to me that a lot of the abstract paintings I see in shows and galleries are beginning to look familiar. What's touted as new or different, isn't that new or different!"

"Being different, doesn't make a painting creative either," Claire said. "In my high school, I constantly hear this child or that is so creative until the teacher stifles them with guidelines. It's easy to throw paint arbitrarily and call whatever develops creative painting, but its not creative, it's arbitrary. Abstract or realistic, a painting must have quality to truly be creative."

"It's not a question of whether abstraction is valid," Kate said. "All design is rooted in abstraction, but the cutting-edge art crowd, left abstraction thirty years ago. We're now in the age of shock art. It's insulting. The lunatics have taken over the asylum, and because we're artists, we're supposed to keep a straight face and buy into it!"

"I just read an article in one of the art publications that proclaimed quality art is dead," Veronica said. "What the New York galleries are interested in these days is called, pathetic art!"

When the laughter subsided, Harold said, "Hey, that means I was making good art before I started taking all these workshops!"

As if on cue, everyone turned to me and shouted, "Yeah, Don, we want our money back!"

After dinner, back in the studio, Kate, Veronica, and Claire gathered around Mona as she stood with clasped hands at her table. They all donated words of advice along with paper, paint and brushes.

"It's like you're a doctor and you're about to perform your first operation," Veronica explained.

Paul raised his hands in surgical fashion. "Prepare the brushes!"

"It's really the same process as working smaller," Kate said. She took a two-inch brush, mixed a large puddle of cerulean blue in the palette, held the brush up and made a wide horizontal stroke across the page. Then she handed the brush to Mona.

"What should I do now?" Mona pleaded.

"Counter balance," Claire said.

Mona reached down and made a tepid stroke on her paper, then another, then a larger one. Surrounded by compatriots, two inch brush in one hand, double martini in the other, Mona began painting, cursing, asking for input. Suddenly she burst out, "I'm doing it. I love it!"

The room erupted in cheers!

Paul held a finger in the air. "Quiet please, you're disturbing the other patients!"

Around ten o'clock, I cleaned out my palette and called it a night, leaving the six working at their tables. I don't know how late they painted, but my bedroom was just down the hall from the studio and long after I'd turned off the lights, a roar of laughter shattered my tranquility!

Tuesday morning I was a few minutes late walking up to the main house for breakfast. No need to hurry, I thought, I'll probably be eating alone. I opened the screened back door and stepped into the dining room. There were six silhouettes seated around our antique table, sleepy-eyed, yawning, talking and laughing. Mona sat between Paul and Harold. On her face there was something I hadn't seen before. She was smiling!

When class convened an hour later, all semblance of foolishness evaporated. The six metamorphosed into model students throughout the day. That evening after we'd finished our dessert, and ambled back to the studio, the metamorphosis completed itself. For twenty minutes, the room would be as quiet as a carload of librarians, then someone would make a comment followed by a retort or sarcastic remark, and the windows would rattle with laughter.

Kate leaned over Harold's shoulder while he sat engrossed in his work. "Harold, what are those things growing out of the dog's head?"

"That's a deer!"

Claire looked up from an art book cradled in her lap. "Does anyone know what 'in the collection of the artist' means?"

"Yeah," Veronica said, "it means the painting didn't sell."

"I'm thinking of writing a book on modern architecture," Paul said. "I'm going to call it, *The Zen of Aluminum!*"

After the laughter subsided, the studio settled back to silence.

"Harold," Veronica said, "you're always sketching. How did you acquire the habit?"

"I had a teacher who preached the virtues of sketching to train the eye. One of the tips he gave me was to make contour drawings without looking at your sketch. He said he would take a small sketchpad and pencil to a bar or restaurant, put the pad in his baggy pants pocket, and make sketches of patrons in his pants."

"I'll bet that raised an eyebrow from the waitress," Claire said. "How often did he check to see if he had lead in his pencil?"

Around eight thirty, Kate threw down her brush. "To hell with art, who wants yogurt?"

Everyone placed an order. Veronica volunteered to go along, and off they drove into the night. Shortly, a hush reclaimed the studio and the deserters were all but forgotten.

In half an hour the sounds of a car could be heard pulling up outside, and a moment later the door flew open. Kate apologized for not being able to locate yogurt. Then she announced that she had brought us pickled pigs feet instead. The laughter waned when Veronica produced contents of a bag as evidence that she wasn't joking.

"Harold, Paul," Kate said, "try one. It won't hurt you!"

"That's what they told the pig!"

"Mona, this is your week to try something new, how about it?"

"Remember what was said yesterday, about different not necessarily being good?"

"I knew it!" Paul blurted out. "A correlation between pigs feet and art!"

Mona pointed her brush at me. "Ask Don, he's from the south. I'll bet he's one of those…what do you call them…roughnecks!"

"That's redneck," I said, and the windows shook again!

Wednesday, I expected my night owls to be running out of gas, but all day they were as inquisitive and industrious as ever. When four o'clock came, our day-students scurried off, Eliot appeared with ice and we continued working until dinner. Sitting around the cherry wood table, the six decided it was time for critique.

"If my work's going to be degraded," Paul said, "I'd just as soon hear it from someone who knows what he's talking about."

"Oh," Claire said, "I thought Don was going to give the critique!"

Like I said, I should have been a doctor.

Back in the studio, work was matted, glasses refilled, and chairs were placed in a semi-circle around my table. I began by explaining my thoughts on the value of a group critique. "I try to point out both the merits and flaws in the painting and suggest possible remedies. The real benefit of a group critique is that we can learn from other artists' struggles, as well as our own."

These platitudes were delivered in an elegant and uplifting manner, and I dare say, it took all of two minutes from that moment for the proceedings to descend into pandemonium!

The first painting up was Harold's nicely handled, if somewhat predictable farm scene, complete with red barn and silo. After pointing out the virtues and problems, I did not say I would now like to relinquish all control of the critique! I did not say that, but looking back, I might as well have, because what I did say was, "If anyone has a comment on the work, please speak up!" The glowing expression on Kate's face told me I had made a mistake even as the words fell from my mouth.

"Harold," Kate beamed, "is that a phallic symbol in your painting?"

Claire's brows shot up. "Ever notice that the silo's always the center of attention in a barn scene?"

Veronica joined the fray. "Placement is everything!"

Laughing hysterically, they all hugged and high-fived. The three of them began trading one-liners like machine gun fire!

"Pretty optimistic proportions!"

"Well, not all silos are the same!"

Between gasps of laughter, tears running down her cheeks, Veronica paused to catch her breath.

"Mona," she asked, "what do you think of the silo?"

All eyes turned to Mona and for an instant, an uneasy anticipation filled the room.

Mona's eyes sharpened, she paused to pull on her martini. "Tell us Harold," she said, "where will this painting be hung?"

Waves of laughter shook the studio! For miles around, lights flipped on, dogs howled, and babies cried.

The sleepy little town of Greenville, New York would have to wait a little longer for bed. The night was young, and the critique had just begun!

Thursday evening during dinner, Eliot stopped by our table to remind us that this was our last night together. All of us had made travel arrangements to leave the next day after class. He also announced that he had a short slide presentation of instructors who would be teaching at the Arms the following season, and asked if we'd like to view the slides in the studio after dinner. His invitation was accepted with a great deal of enthusiasm by my six dining companions, so right away I knew he was in trouble.

After dinner, everyone excused themselves and hurried off to the studio, while I lagged behind. Eliot's a nice guy, so I thought the least I could do was give him fair warning. I found him in his office.

"Eliot, can I talk to you a minute?"

"Sure." He motioned me to have a seat.

"Eliot, do you have any idea what you're in for tonight?"

"Oh, I've got a pretty good idea, but you know, my entire staff just loves them. They say we've never had a more personable group to stay here. You should have heard the conversation Kate had yesterday with the chef. Something to do with pigs feet!"

"I know they're sweethearts," I said, "but when they get together in the studio at night, there's a lot of…of…"

"Chemistry," Eliot said.

"Exactly, and keep in mind that chemistry is what causes explosions!"

"There could be one other hitch," Eliot said. "Did you happen to notice the distinguished looking older couple seated across from you in the dining room?"

"I suppose so, why?"

"They're staying here tonight and overheard me telling your table about the slide show. Afterwards, they approached me and asked if they could sit in on the presentation. What do you think?"

"Let me put it this way, how much do you depend on repeat business?"

Eliot smiled in resignation. "I couldn't say no to them, so I guess I'll have to chance it."

I got up and headed for the door, stopped and looked back. "Eliot," I said, "Good luck!"

Walking from the rear of the main house back to the painting studio, I saw Mona alone on the studio steps.

"Come sit with me before we go in," she said.

As I took a seat beside her, I could see a river of feelings pulling the lines of her face.

"I wanted to thank you personally for letting our group have fun at night." She paused to taste the double in her hand, her liquid eyes filled with emotion. "I'm not funny like the rest, in fact most people don't like me."

"Mona, that's not…"

She put her hand on my arm. "Please, let me finish," she said. "For too long, I've gotten no pleasure from life, but this week I've learned that I can still have fun, and even more, I can be fun to be with. I still have some life left, and I'm going to start living it!"

She squeezed my arm; I helped her to her feet and opened the studio door.

Inside, we were greeted by a festive air of anticipation. Eliot and his distinguished guests soon arrived. Introductions were made. Kate offered them a drink while Eliot set up the projector. On his cue, I flicked the lights to signal the program's beginning. Everyone took their seats; I turned off the lights. Through the darkness a large white rectangle of light projected on the screen. Eliot commenced his introduction above the hum of the projector. Somewhere between his first and second sentence, a hand silhouette of a flapping bird appeared on the screen, then an elephant, followed by a rabbit.

The stage was set, the mood was right. I sat back and made myself comfortable. This was going to be good!

The first slide projected was of a photo-realistic painting. Eliot spoke on the merits of the work and listed the accolades of the artist. His presentation was professional, his delivery flawless, but then he made a fatal error. I spotted it right away. For a brief moment, he let the slide project in silence. From out of the darkness I recognized Paul's voice.

"Wow, talk about anal retention!"

Above the laughter, Harold joined in. "Until now, I never realized how loose my architectural renderings were!"

Mona began making snoring sounds!

Eliot gathered himself, pushed the forward button and the slide tray advanced. Once again, a tightly rendered still life appeared on screen.

Suddenly sarcastic darts came flying through the darkness from all directions. I couldn't always identify the source, but all six made impressive contributions!

"Ahhhh...he's not so tight! Look at the veins in leaf twenty-seven in the bottom left of the painting. They're almost gestural!"

"Yeah, he really let go!"

"I love it when an artist gets juicy!"

I should say here that the comments, though biting, were not aimed at any particular artist or direction. It was open season, and every instructor represented took their turn walking the gauntlet; a shooting gallery, but all in fun.

The next set of slides was from an abstract painter of lofty reputation. Eliot, always the optimist, gave a brief synopsis of the work, hoping to regain some control over the proceedings, but I could tell he was now resigned to the assault.

The first slide in the set was a non-objective painting that I recognized as a top award winner in a recent national show. Mona's sandpaper voice sliced through the darkness.

"Too many drugs in the sixties!"

"Man," Kate said, "how'd you like to see the psychological profile on that guy?"

"I think this painting comes from his Prozac Period!"

As Eliot introduced another artist on the menu, I glanced over my shoulder, hoping to catch the reaction of the older couple seated behind me. What must they be thinking? They had come to see a slide presentation on contemporary art and were now eyewitnesses to a mugging! There, in the back of the room, two shadowy figures were visible but it was impossible to detect their expressions.

The following slide series was from a landscape painter, highly regarded as an artist and teacher. "These are demonstration paintings done here on location," Eliot said. The first painting was a suggestion of a stand of trees, expressed as a fluid minimal statement.

"That's going to be good when it's finished."

"I'll bet I can guess what's written below the title."

"What?"

"In the collection of the artist!"

The next slide fell to everyone's applause. It was a gestural interpretation of a barn scene, complete with cows, fences and silo! When the roar of the crowd simmered, Veronica called out. "Mona, what do you think of that silo?"

"I've seen bigger!"

As I said, the comments were mischievous and irreverent, but all made in fun. At least I'd like to think so because the next set of slides were mine!

The room erupted with stamping feet, whistles and cheers. The first painting projected was a back view of a nude, painted in predominantly cool colors.

"Don's art certainly follows his interest!"

"Where'd you paint her, Alaska?"

"Titles please!"

"Blue moon!"

"The Zen of Gluteus Maximus!"

"Frozen Assets!"

Eliot's thumb must have become fatigued working the remote control, because the pace of the slide advance suddenly slowed down. I felt like the clown at a dunking booth. Finally, the last slide was shown and the last barb was thrown!

Eliot thanked all for their undivided attention and received a thundering ovation. Lights flipped on followed by sounds of chatter, chairs shuffling and the clinking of ice cubes. I turned to see the older couple putting on their coats as they talked with Eliot by the door. Soon their conversation ended and the couple departed. I made my way over to Eliot as he stood rewinding an extension cord.

"So," I grimaced, "what did they say?"

Eliot let me dangle in suspense for a moment before he broke into a grin.

"They wanted to know if there was still time to sign up for your class!"

A Beautiful Model

Monday morning my director, Diane, drove me through a congested snarl of autos and taxis, honking, stopping and lurching ahead, maneuvering for position. I'd been in New York City before, but this was my first time there to teach.

" Diane, tell me about our models."

Concentrating on traffic, Diane spoke without looking over. "Teresa has modeled for various figure and portrait classes in the city for a number of years," she said. "She's getting a little older, and she's not what you would call beautiful or perfectly built, but she's dependable, strikes a good pose, and is always a class favorite." Diane interrupted herself to slam on brakes as a yellow cab swerved in front of her.

"Aside from modeling, Teresa is a volunteer for the humane society and goes into some of the roughest neighborhoods in New York to rescue stray dogs and cats. I think you'll like her."

"I like her already. How about the other model?"

"I haven't worked with Renee before, but she comes highly recommended." Diane spoke as she changed lanes in perfect time to cut off the yellow taxi. "I understand she's strikingly beautiful and has modeled for some of the top artists in the city."

Thirty minutes later, as I was setting up my paint gear in class, Diane came over with two young women in robes to introduce me. If riding through the city of New York had been impressive, it was nothing compared to the sight of the young goddess that now stood before me. Renee was in her mid-twenties and stunningly attractive. Her emerald eyes and turned up nose were accentuated by high cheekbones and framed by a cascade of auburn hair. I surmised the woman standing next to Renee was Teresa, and though she seemed perfectly comfortable, I couldn't blame her if she felt a little plain in comparison to the vision beside her. I guessed Teresa to be in her late thirties, and while not exactly pretty, her face had agreeable lines and a bone structure that would lend itself to painting. Teresa gave me a pleasant smile and stuck out her hand to greet me.

I introduced myself to both of them and broke into my usual spiel. "We'll start off with twenty minutes of two-minute gesture poses. Try to give us a variety of standing, seated, active and inactive gestures. The poses I like best are the ones that appear as if you're not posing at all, but are comfortable and natural….

Renee interrupted. "My poses reflect the philosophy of Tai Chi. You are familiar with the study of cerebral esthetics in the oriental versus occidental genre?"

"Uhhh…I'm not sure," I mumbled, wondering what the proper response should be. "No doubt, every artist you model for has a little different…"

Renee broke in again. "I've modeled extensively for Rudolph Bozeman. He says my poses are ethereal in a frenetic sense."

I nodded, feigning comprehension. "What I'm looking for in a …"

Once more Renee stopped me. "My body is an instrument that implements the universal forces harmonizing nature."

As best I could, I shook off befuddlement and tried to imply comprehension. I knew she was speaking English, but without a translator, I couldn't understand a word she was saying! I looked down at my watch. "It's time to get started," I said. "If you'll each take a podium, I'm sure we'll do fine."

The model stands were on opposite sides of the room, with half the class forming a semi-circle around each one. As Teresa and Renee made their way to the platforms, I announced to the group that I was setting the timer, and we were about to commence twenty minutes of a warm-up drawing session.

Teresa stepped up on her podium and removed her robe. Shifting weight to one hip, she crossed arms with hands on her shoulders, and tilted her head to one side. She looked like a Michelangelo sculpture as she froze into a classic, understated pose. Instantly the students around her began to draw. Turning my head to the other podium, I expected to see Renee striking a pose as well, but to my surprise she had disrobed in front of the stand and was now moving about in a slow motion Oriental dance, emitting a steady, "Ahhhummm..."

The students around her exchanged curious glances, not sure if they were supposed to begin their drawings or not. I hurried over to her as she kicked and sliced the air with carefully controlled motions. Renee looked right through me, as if I wasn't there. "Ahhummm...."

"Renee," I waved at her, "we're ready to begin!"

Suddenly, she came to a halt, blinked her eyes into focus and shot me a steely glare. "Dexterous supposition is optimum for Tai Chi!" she snapped, and in a huff stepped up on the podium. Assuming a wide crouching stance, Renee remained stationary for an instant; then she began twisting her upper torso until her top half practically faced backwards. Arms began to coil into interlocking knots around her contorted torso, and her head turned, parrot-like, looking over her shoulder. She looked over to me. "I can hold this pose for 40 minutes," she said, as if daring me to challenge her.

"That's great, but these are two minute poses please." Renee gave me a withering look and fell into a trance.

In two minutes I called out, "Change," and there was a muffled flapping as the class collectively turned pages of their newsprint pads.

Teresa took a seated position with one knee up, and wrapped an arm around it. Again she froze into a graceful pose.

Renee gradually unraveled back to a Tai Chi stance before gyrating down to lie on her back, twisting one arm around her head to grab an ear. With the other arm, she reached over her head and clasped the opposing ear. Her legs were interlaced into a corkscrew, and she began to crank them up toward the ceiling.

I walked down the line of students working at their easels, but offered no critiques. I couldn't tell if the drawings were accurate or not. I'd never seen arms and legs bent into these arrangements before.

Two minutes later, I asked the models to change again. I walked over to the podium as Renee untied herself. "Renee, for variety, could we have a few poses that are more relaxed?"

Her brow straightened to a line. "I must have the freedom to internally synthesize emotional and holistic space," she said.

"Let me explain," I said. "My response to a pose is on a visual level. I'm concerned with…"

"Watch this," she cut me off, melting down on one knee. Tucking her chin into her chest, she wrapped one arm around her back, the other around her neck, then began to twist herself into a figure eight from the knees up.

"Is that relaxing?" I asked.

"Totally," she said.

When the warm-up session was over, I called the class to gather around my table for the morning demonstration. After I'd finished my lesson, we took a coffee break before setting up for a long pose. I placed a chair on a podium and asked Teresa to have a seat. She sat down and leaned her weight on the right arm of the chair.

"Now turn your head to the left," I said. "Perfect!" I positioned a spotlight to create a shadow pattern on her face and set the timer as the class began their paintings. Then I walked to the other podium. "Has anybody seen Renee?"

"She's out in the hall," someone said.

I stepped out to find Renee rotating on the ball of one foot in slow motion, her other foot clasped with both hands as she chanted, "Ahummmm...."

"Excuse me, Renee, we're ready to start."

Renee continued to flow around in a circular motion, but now with arms extended high above her head, palms arced down like wings. "Ahhummmm...."

"Renee!" Her eyes popped open and she lowered her arms, giving me a frown. "We're ready to begin, but before we go in, let me explain what I'm after. My teaching concepts are based on light and shadow patterns that flow across..."

Renee stopped me. "Obviously, you're unaware of the Tai Chi teachings that integrate internal motivations with an external response!"

"Uh, no, I'm not familiar with..."

"Perhaps your painting concepts are overly complex. Have you considered three dimensional integrity without empiricism?"

""No, Renee, I haven't, but we don't have time to discuss it now. The class is waiting and I'd like you to hold a pose I can work with!"

"Your concepts are not conducive to Tai Chi.."

I held up a hand and motioned her to follow me. Renee fell silent and marched into class. She stood with folded arms as I placed a chair on the podium. "Just sit down comfortably and lean on one arm for support."

"I don't understand," she growled.

It looks silly when I do it, but I stepped up to show her what I wanted.

"Something like this."

"If you could transmit your concepts subliminally, I can synthesize your cerebral esthetic," she said.

"Renee, I've never been very good at transmitting my cerebral…"

Just then a cell phone beeped, and Renee reached down into her bag beside the podium. "Can't talk now," she spoke in pauses. "You wouldn't believe me…don't ask…worse…wrong century!" Renee glanced over to me and I pointed at my wristwatch. "I'll tell you later. Ciao!"

Renee replaced her cell phone and plopped down in the chair. "How's this?' she huffed.

"Fine." I hoped she could assimilate my current subliminal transmission! I turned and looked at Teresa, posed like a delicate piece of porcelain on the podium across the room. She didn't move a muscle, but her eyes lifted to meet mine, and she gave me a wink.

After class that evening I pyramided the pillows on my hotel room bed and sat back to ponder the day's events. I jumped as the phone rang with Martha on the line. We had exchanged our usual lovebird banter when she asked, "So, are the models beautiful?"

I thought for a moment before I answered. "One of them is!"

Stage Fright

Six or eight times a year, I'm asked to do a live painting demonstration for a large art group or watercolor society. Invariably I'm asked the same question, and invariably I tell the same lie. "Don, do you get nervous doing a live painting demonstration in front of a large group of people?"

"No..." I answer nonchalantly, "I've done it a thousand times..."

Then the night of the program arrives and those same old thoughts and fears begin to wedge their way into my mind. The worst part is always the last few minutes before I take the stage; my palms sweat, anxiety locks my stomach. The announcer begins my introduction and my mind races as the lonely stage awaits. One last time, I search the crowd and ask myself, "What would she look like, would I recognize her after all these years? Even worse, what would I do if I did?"

The announcer finishes my introduction and I step up on stage. I step up to the perfect trap. Irrational stage fright you say…well, stage fright, yes, but irrational…. Let me explain.

The year was 1969, my senior year of high school. That year the world was spinning out of control in places like Washington D.C., Berkley, and Southeast Asia. I knew the ugly world was out there waiting, but I had one year left before I had to face it, and I was having a pretty good year.

One day, I walked into my English class and was told that we were to proceed in an orderly fashion to the school auditorium, where we were in for a special treat. As we were getting up to go, the teacher added the usual veiled threats about being on our best behavior. No foolishness of any kind would be tolerated.

When we arrived at the giant room, other classes of students were filing in as well. Walking down the aisle, I noticed a lone, black-clad figure on stage, sitting with her back to the audience. I took my seat next to one of my best friends, Mike Payne. We had no idea what sort of torture the teachers had thought up for us, but misery loves company, and so we took our places shoulder to shoulder. There must have been 50 rows of seats in the auditorium. Our class was one of the first ones in, and so we were herded down front, right in the middle, at about aisle three.

Once the auditorium was filled, the vice-principal, Mr. Gaines, stepped up to the podium on the corner of the stage. His steely glare muffled the crowd, before he gave fair warning. "Absolutely no disorderly conduct will be tolerated." He meant business and we knew it. You could have heard a mosquito sneeze. Then, like a storm passing, he brightened, and then beamed. "We are in for a special treat. Your fellow senior and class valedictorian, Sondra Beecham, has graciously agreed to perform one of the all-time English classics for our entertainment!"

I didn't know Sondra Beecham. I knew who she was, of course, everybody knew Sondra. As I said, she was valedictorian of our class, not to mention president of the student council, glee club, French club etc. Aside from brains, Sondra was well-tended; her father was a local politician, and her family had money. The word was, colleges like Vanderbilt, Georgia Tech and Radcliffe clambered over each other to offer Sondra a scholarship. If Sondra was a bit aloof, well so be it, she deserved to be. Sondra was the toast of Davidson High, and every teacher's dream. Yes, Sondra had brains, she had clout, and as things turned out, she had one more thing, a white hot, unabridged hatred for, DON ANDREWS. I couldn't really blame her.

"Without further adieu," the vice principal blathered, "I give you Sondra Beecham, performing her own rendition of Edgar Allen Poe's classic poem, "The Raven!" Glowing with anticipation, Mr. Gaines clicked his heels smartly and turned to strut offstage. My buddy, Mike, glanced at me and rolled his eyes. I returned a bewildered smile.

Ever so slowly, the seated figure on stage began to rise and turn to face the crowd. Sondra had her hair frizzed out like a banshee. Her face was covered in pancake makeup. Painted eyes were black orbs, with one teardrop painted just below the corner of her left eye. Her dress was a macabre black garment, torn and hanging loosely on her arms and flowing down around the floor. For a moment she stood glaring at the crowd, then like a shot, she was off!!

"Once," she shouted and instantly paused, then tying the rest of the first line together, "upon a midnight dreary!" She paused a second time, stepped back and pantomimed wiggling fingers, as she lowered her voice, "While I pondered... weak and weary." Then another pause, this time with brows arched, her voice rising in a slow, steady cadence, as her right foot banged out time on the stage floor.

"Suddenly, there came a rapping!!!" Her voice lowered impressively, "Tapping," she shouted, "Tapping," she bellowed, and then blasted, "Tapping at my chamber door!!!"

My friend Mike and I exchanged curious expressions of amusement but were instantly pulled back by Sondra's voice blaring anew, "while I pondered... nearly napping," she whispered, head cocked, praying hands bracing the side of her pancake face.

"Suddenly," she shrieked, "there came a rapping," pausing again for emphasis, "Tapping," she exclaimed, frizzed hair and dark eyes flaring, arms flailing, right foot pounding, "RAPPING AT MY CHAMBER DOOR!!"

At that instant, with the perfect timing of an unrehearsed response, my buddy Mike leaned over and whispered in my ear, "It's probably the dogcatcher."

Mike's comment caught me totally off guard. I lunged forward to catch my outburst! In a situation where any sound or movement would be instantly detected by a host of teachers and principals, I struggled to control myself. This was a big moment for Sondra, and no one was going to mess it up! I clawed my arms, I chewed my tongue, but the more I struggled and the more Sondra shouted, the funnier it became.

"The Raven" is a long poem, exceedingly. Sondra had just delivered the first two verses. There were 32 left to go, I know, later, for my own clarification, I looked it up. I tried to gulp down guffaws before they burst out, I slobbered, I snorted, but there was only so much I could do.

Sondra did me no favors; she ranted and raved, shouted and howled, as my chair danced under restrained emotion. Every thirty seconds or so, I'd feel my stomach muscles begin to relax and I'd think the storm was passing, but then Sondra would return to that relentless refrain, "Rapping and tapping," and I was off again! On and on she went, on and on I followed.

Finally, mercifully, it was over. The audience applauded, appropriately. The vice principal, Mr. Gaines, marched smartly to the podium, stepped up to the mike, smiled to Sondra and congratulated her on a thrilling performance. Then he squared his shoulders; eyes squinted like twin lasers aimed directly at me. He cleared his throat and announced that everyone was to return to their assigned classes. Then he paused, "Except for *Don Andrews* and *Mike Payne.*"

The next minute passed with a rumble of teenagers filing past us. Without turning my head, I whispered, "How much trouble do you think we're in?" I caught Mike's shrug out of the corner of my eye. "Are you kidding," he groaned, "this is the ball game." When the last student stepped out and the metal door slammed shut, for an instant, the great room fell silent.

Like flapping vultures, a host of teachers, aides and Mr. Gaines, descended upon us from every direction, shouting and snarling. Certain punishment was coming, swift, harsh, brutal, and yet, there seemed to be a look of frustration behind the viciousness in their eyes. No matter what they said or did, it wouldn't be enough. Their bloodlust would go unsatisfied; there was no capital punishment in high school.

Like snapping hounds, they climbed over each other to get to us. Emerging through the middle of the pack, black eyes still boiling, electric hair askew, spewing hatred and vengeance directly at me, was Sondra Beecham. I tried to explain, I tried to apologize but they wanted no explanation, they wanted retribution!

"I'll get you," Sondra blared in my face. Over and over she vowed, "I'll get even, just you wait," till finally they dragged us away.

Thirty years have passed since that day, and they say time is a great healer. Somehow, I don't think that applies to Sondra and me. I still see her black eyes flaming, and I hear her vows of revenge ringing in my ears.

To this day, when the hour of my painting demonstration arrives, my introduction is complete and the applause settles down, I step up on stage and survey the crowd. I know someday, somewhere, sooner or later; I'll look down with horror on a middle-aged woman in the front row, smiling at me with a familiar flame of vengeance burning bright in her eyes. She'll have me right where she wants me. There in the audience will be Sondra Beecham, rapping, tapping, tapping, at my chamber door!

Bed and Breakfast

There are two types of travelers in this world, those who enjoy the social aspects of staying at a bed and breakfast, and those who prefer the anonymity of a hotel room. I understand why many people enjoy making new acquaintances on the road, and prefer not to eat alone. However, because I'm usually teaching when I'm traveling, and spend most of my day intermixing with a variety of people, I usually opt for the seclusion and quiet of a local hotel. In a town of any size, that's not a problem. There are plenty of hotels to choose from. However, occasionally I'll be teaching in a small town and the hotels are few or bad, and sometimes there's no choice at all.

One spring not so long ago, I was scheduled to teach in a town so small, the workshop director told me there was no hotel to put me in, so she'd booked me in the one B&B available.

"Don't worry," she said, "you'll be comfortable there, and luckily, the only restaurant that serves dinner is just across the street."

As it turned out, the bed and breakfast was an elegant old three-story Victorian house, completely remodeled, and meticulously groomed. The managing owners, Mr. and Mrs. Reed, were a delightful older couple, well read and traveled. The Reeds were able to carry a conversation on any subject with effortless ease.

"What I enjoy most about running a bed and breakfast," Mr. Reed told me as I was checking in, "is the stimulating conversations with so many diverse and interesting people. There's always something new to learn."

I followed behind Mr. Reed as he led me up a banistered stairway to my room. His wing-tips were two-toned antiques, out of which rose silk stockings and bony ankles.

"Breakfast is served at seven," he said. "I look forward to learning more about you then."

The next morning, I entered the chandeliered breakfast room to find a table of strangers. The aroma of thick-sliced bacon filled the air. Mr. Reed made introductions as I found my seat, then he asked me to tell a little about myself. To be honest, I would have preferred to have coffee and a quiet breakfast mulling over the paper, but I liked Mr. Reed, and obviously, he felt it was one of his primary duties as a good host to prod his guests into interaction.

As Mr. Reed predicted, my breakfast companions were indeed an interesting and diverse group. We made small talk on a number of subjects. Everyone gradually grew more talkative until the table bounded with discussions on art, current events and travel. As he served, Mr. Reed beamed with pride at the flowing conversation he had inspired.

After breakfast, back in my room, while I gathered my gear for class, I scolded myself for being so set in my ways. Mr. Reed was right, there are a lot of interesting people out there, if you take the time to get to know them.

Following class that afternoon, I went back to my room for a rest before getting ready to go across the street for a quiet dinner. Closing the door to my second-story room, I'd descended only a few steps down the banistered stairway when I heard a baritone voice blaring from the hallway below.

"Beef tips," I heard a voice boom so loud it could have been cannon fire. "Trust me partner, no matter if the stock market gains or slips, people eat beef tips!"

I slowed my pace of descent to catch more clearly the ongoing conversation.

"I've got more tips than a waitress on Saturday night!!! HA HA...."

I didn't recognize the booming voice, but the reply was unmistakably Mr. Reed. "How witty," he said.

Instantly, the loudspeaker voice vibrated the walls around me. "You don't know it, but more people eat beef tips in these three states, than any other states in the country."

"Is that so?" Mr. Reed replied.

"Per capita, of course!"

"Of course."

"I always say at home or on trips, people love beef tips!" The jingle was followed by an explosion of deafening laughter, to which I heard Mr. Reed dutifully respond, "That's catchy."

Rounding the stairway to the final flight, the audible level of the stranger's voice grew even more impressive.

"Hey, partner, you like that, I've got a million of 'em. Here's one my little wife, Mary Lou, thought up. If you're looking for a burger that won't expand your hips, try beef tips!"

Again, the ridiculous jingle was followed by waves of self-satisfied guffaws!

"Clever," was Mr. Reed's strained response. "Quite clever indeed."

I couldn't help but laugh to myself at Mr. Reed's predicament. I wondered what he'd say about stimulating conversations with interesting people, *now*? My thoughts were severed by the blathering voice I was steadily descending toward.

"Yeah, partner, that Mary Lou's a stitch. She's always saying beef tips may be brown, but they bring in a lot of green!" followed by an obnoxious laugh. HA HA HA....

I bet myself that poor Mr. Reed was learning enough about beef tips to last a lifetime. I took a few more steps down the stairs until two silhouetted figures came into view. There, in the hallway, stood a refrigerator-sized hulk in a wrinkled suit, cigar in hand, towering over a figure with his back to me, that was obviously Mr. Reed.

"Yeah, that Mary Lou can fry up a plate of beef tips that'll make you bark at the moon!"

"Is that so," Mr. Reed nodded his head and tried to sound impressed.

I'd reached the bottom of the carpeted stairs and stepped down to the hardwood floor of the mansion hallway.

"I'm sorry your wife, Mary Lou, couldn't be with us," Mr. Reed said.

"Naw, Mary Lou's not much on travel," the Goliath barked so loud that Mr. Reed's gray hair blew in the breeze. "Traveling makes Mary Lou irregular, if you know what I mean."

I tucked my head, picked up my pace, and stared at the floor straight ahead, hoping the discussion of Mary Lou's personal problems would occupy the two men long enough for me to slip past them and out the door.

Whoever named tennis shoes "sneakers" never walked across a waxed hardwood floor, because every step I took emitted an all too noticeable squeak. I averted my eyes and set a course as far away from the two men as possible, hoping the deafening details of Mary Lou's irregularity would drown out my presence.

As I approached, suddenly Mr. Reed spun around to face me. "Mr. Andrews, are you on your way out?"

"Yes, I thought I'd step across the street for dinner."

"Oh, splendid," Mr. Reed perked up, his glazed eyes suddenly bright. "Our new guest, Mr. Hargrove here, was just saying he'd like to try that restaurant. I'm sure you wouldn't mind a little company!"

The mammoth-sized Bigfoot threw an arm around my shoulder. His breath smelled of cigar and cognac.

"Hey, partner, what da ya say we go rustle up a couple orders of beef tips?"

Critical Analysis

One of the benefits of flying a lot is that the airlines send you coupons called first-class upgrades. You can exchange these coupons to fly in the first class section of the plane at no extra charge. Put in practical terms, that means you get to fly in a seat designed to fit a medium sized torso, plus have a decent meal, complete with tablecloth, and a free drink or two. I save my upgrades for cross-country flights, so when I arrive at my destination, there is still some feeling left in my lower extremities.

I had just finished a workshop week in California and was dropped off at the airport on Saturday morning. Ahead of me was an eight-hour flight back to Boston, with one stop in Cincinnati. When I arrived at the gate counter, the area was swarming with travelers. It was going to take five upgrade coupons to ride the entire flight first class, but

I'd had a good week and decided to treat myself. I rummaged through my bag, produced the coupons for the ticket agent and presto, I was delivered from a cold sandwich, peanuts and a Coke, to Chicken Florentine and white wine, or was it red? I can never remember.

As I was getting settled in my seat, my traveling companion arrived and we exchanged nods. He had the look and manner of a man to whom leather seats and first-class treatment were expected. I could tell he had no idea of the horrors about to take place, just a few feet behind us, in what is commonly known as coach. He was a rather unique looking man, tall and lean, well-dressed to the point of flamboyant, but the thing I noticed was the turquoise ascot; this was no salesman from Toledo.

When the stewardess came by to ask if we'd like a drink before take-off, he slowly raised his head to her, and spoke with disdain in his voice. "Have you a decent Chardonnay?"

He put his briefcase on his lap and got out several sheets of paper. Instantly he began writing, mumbling, scratching out, flipping the page and writing again. When the stewardess reappeared with his drink, he gave her a disapproving pout for disturbing his thought, then with a wave of his hand, dismissed her without thanks.

The next twenty minutes passed uneventfully. After takeoff, my neighbor resumed his writing, muttering and flipping of pages. I listened to the co-pilot announcing the altitude to which we'd be climbing, scenic points of interest, visible from the other side of the plane, the temperature outside of 40 degrees below zero, and wondered who exactly would benefit from that information.

Suddenly, my industrious companion slapped himself on the thigh. From the corner of my eye, I could see his large head pop up, then dart back to his paper, then pop up again, desperately searching for someone to be as pleased with him as he was with himself. I turned to look and our eyes made contact. There was a pause as he regained his composure.

"I beg your pardon," he said, peering down his long nose at me, "might I trouble you for your opinion?"

"On what?"

"I've written an article of analysis and need the benefit of a second opinion, while the work is fresh in my mind. It's but a few paragraphs, would you mind the intrusion?"

"Not at all."

"Perhaps I should explain myself first," he said. "I'm a journalist for the Times. I specialize in critical analysis of visual arts. I've just completed my written opinion of an upcoming exhibition and would like a response from an impartial party, so to speak."

"You're an art critic?"

"Correct, but don't concern yourself. You needn't be schooled in the field of visual arts. I merely desire your reaction to my article."

I was about a half-second away from blurting out that I was an artist, and wasn't it a coincidence, blah,blah,blah, when a two-by-four, wet mop, stop sign and blinking lights of consciousness were able to collectively close the gaping hole that was my open mouth. Popeyed, it hit me; there was a lifetime opportunity here. "You're an art critic?" I repeated, trying to buy time while I plotted my course.

"Yes, yes," he snapped. "If I might intrude upon you for a few moments, would you read my opinion and grant me the benefit of yours? As I've stated, you need not concern yourself with the implications of the article, it is your response to it that I wish to obtain."

"Okay."

He handed me a single page with a few handwritten paragraphs. A bony finger sprang up with a final word of instruction. "Do not equivocate!"

Equivocate, I thought to myself. Equivocate. I haven't equivocated in years! I switched on the overhead lamp and began to read. The subject of the article was the opening of an exhibition of oil paintings, in Los Angeles, by an artist I didn't recognize.

From the opening sentence, a mean-spirited, authoritative sarcasm oozed down the page, sprinkled with fancy words and clumsy humor; each paragraph more acidic than its predecessor. The last paragraph ended with, "Normally the artist dies and his work lives on after him; unfortunately, in this instance the reverse is true."

I sat the page on my lap and paused to evaluate more closely the passenger next to me. He was impeccably dressed. The cream-colored summer suit wasn't off the rack. I'll even go so far as to say that the ascot worked. However, beneath the fashion statement was not a man, but what appeared to be the head of an extremely large, uncommonly pale, desperately in need of a sunlamp, lizard. I don't mean the flower garden variety. I'm talking about one of those things you see in the National Geographic specials taken on Guam; slanted forehead, incredibly wide mouth, no lips and two endless rows of tiny pointed teeth.

He sat without speaking, his facial expression anxious, arms coiled high across his chest. I wasn't sure how best to draw him out, so I decided to make him wait. He faced me with gleaming eyes, his tongue darted impatiently.

"Well?" he finally blurted.

"Don't expect a Christmas card from the artist," I said, camouflaging my disdain. "You beat him up pretty good."

"Yes, yes, yes," he jeered. "Is there cohesion in my analysis of the work?"

"If nothing else, it's consistent."

"Good...good...did you find the cadence pleasing, the use of metaphors and levity stimulating?"

Careful, Don, go slow...the first rule of fishing is patience, but by then I knew what he wanted to hear. "The rhythm and humor make the article entertaining," I said, with an innocent expression plastered across my face, "but I certainly wouldn't go out of my way to see the show."

Delighted, his hairless brows spiked. "And if you were the director of the exhibition, how might you react?"

"I'd be mortified."

Hearing my prediction, his mouth turned up at the corners and a high-pitched AAAHHHHH... emerged, as he clapped his anemic claws in tiny applause.

I returned his paper and offered a little bait. "Aren't you concerned about the negative response your article is bound to create?"

Gyrating eyes narrowed and his mouth curled to a sneer. "A negative response, as you put it, is precisely what I intend to evoke!"

"I'm sorry," I said, "I don't quite follow you," hoping he'd elaborate.

"Oh, it's hardly relevant, but thank you for your time."

I could see he was about to dismiss me. I grappled to pique his interest. If there's one thing I know about the human species, it's that we are all engaged when the topic of conversation turns to our work. I'm the world's worst...tell me you like my paintings and I'll buy you lunch and give you the keys to my car. "Forgive me," I said, consciously omitting the '*you pompous bastard.*' "Obviously, a person with your knowledge and position would find it boring to discuss art with someone like me. I've always been interested in the arts, but I really don't understand what constitutes the label of art these days." I hoped my flattery would overcome his resistance.

"Well, my friend, your sentiments are at the very core of what I do!"

"And what is that?"

"I tell the public what art is, and more emphatically, what art is NOT!"

With that statement, he let out a self-satisfied hiss, as if he'd caught a fly!

"I hope you won't be offended," I said, "but sometimes when I read a column like yours, the opinions of the critic run so contrary to my own, I can't help wondering if the reviewer is being totally honest."

"An interesting observation young man," he mused. "So, you seek the truth?"

"Yes, I think I do."

He paused for a moment and chuckled to himself. Then he nodded his massive head as if giving himself permission. "Very well," he said, "we shall see how much of the truth you are able to ascertain."

I reeled my head to the aisle. "Stewardess, may I have another drink, and would you please bring one for my friend as well?" Instantly, I snapped my head back to my neighbor. "I hope you won't mind, but I'm a little afraid of flying." As the stewardess arrived with our refills, I continued, "As I was saying, I find the subject of art fascinating, but somewhat baffling as well."

He took a healthy sip, pursing his lipless mouth as he focused his thoughts. Clearly he was enjoying the admiration, and was preparing to expound.

"You see," he said, "society in general feels more or less as you do. The masses hunger for art appreciation, but have no formal education in the Arts, and therefore, possess an innate feeling of incompetence."

"I see, so through your column, you educate the masses as to what art is."

"In a manner of speaking."

"As with the piece I just read?"

"Correct!"

"Do you always give your readers your honest opinion?"

"The key word here is *opinion*. Art, by its very definition, is interpretation."

"Do you ever worry that your opinion may mislead the public or hamper some artist who's trying to make his way?"

"Actually, I find it quite invigorating," he said, as he fingered the paper in his lap.

"But don't you feel a little guilty, putting down some poor artist who…"

"Oh, come, come…" he interrupted, "do put down the violin. Nobody buys good news do they? It's the train wreck people want to read about! Besides, bloodletting is where the fun is!" He paused, gave me a wink and tongued his Chardonnay.

I considered reaching over, getting my poor artist's hands around his scaly neck and submitting to the pleasures of bloodletting, but instead offered my most insincere smile of understanding. "Oh, I can imagine," I said, "but doesn't anyone ever challenge your authority?"

"The uneducated do not challenge authority, my friend, they seek it!" I sat silent for a moment, hoping to convey deep contemplation. My eyes focused on a small red sign just above the cabin door. DO NOT OPEN DURING FLIGHT. Then I turned to face my neighbor again.

"Where did you receive your education in the arts?" I asked.

His self-satisfied expression exploded into laughter. "You mean formally? Oh, dear me, it's been so long I'd nearly forgotten. I went to a small liberal arts college in Northern California."

"Did you study art or art history?"

"Neither," he said. "I was a journalism major. Oh, I took the usual art appreciation courses, enough to get me by, but that has precious little to do with anything!"

"I'm sorry, I don't quite follow you?"

He raised a claw for emphasis. "It's not the study of art, but the study of the art language, that must be cultivated!"

"Art language?"

"Let me see if I can give you an example," he said, and for a moment he fell silent, stroking his sloping forehead. "Let's say you are to review a body of work for critical analysis. The artist may be unknown or renowned, the work, non-objective or realistic, no matter. If you wish to praise the work, you contend in your well-studied opinion, the work manifests an extemporaneous sense of relevance. On the other hand, if you aim to discredit, you contend that in your well-studied opinion, the work evokes no sense of extemporaneous relevance."

Trying to sound impressed, I asked, "But what does extemporaneous sense of relevance mean?"

"That's just it poor boy," he mused, "it doesn't mean anything, or put more aptly, it's meaning could apply to anything. Don't you see, it's the nebulous nature of the choice of words that attracts the elitists and confounds the unwashed masses!" He paused for another quick sip and summoned a serious pose. "The truth is, my column eventually ends up where it belongs, at the bottom of a birdcage. But how I love to hear those pretentious snobs line up to argue on my behalf, while the public sighs in resignation, confused as ever!"

"Where does the artist fit into all this?"

His face contorted as he changed colors, "Ah... the unwitting pawns in my little game! Can you imagine, they work their hearts out trying to gain my favor, yearning for acceptance, anxious to submit to me." His voice dripped with sarcasm, "and then..."

"Then?" I asked.

"Then, their efforts are found to be aesthetically void of ethereal verisimilitudes!" With this statement, his subterranean eyes flashed red as he gleamed a reptilian grin.

I turned my attention once more to the red sign above the cabin door and wondered how long (in his well-studied opinion) it would take to fall 30,000 feet.

"What do you think is the best column you've written?"

"You mean the one I'm proudest of?"

"Yes."

"No doubt, my piece on the Wyeth retrospective a few years back."

"You mean Andrew?"

"Yes, and Jamie as well, to be precise."

"Did you like the work?"

"Are you asking me what I thought, or what I wrote?"

"Both, I suppose."

His boorish tone softened as he paused and looked away. "Anyone could see the work was powerful, honest, I dare say...they moved me deeply. Wyeth has the innate capacity to cross boundaries, to make the viewer see clearer, deeper somehow."

"So, you praised the work in your column?"

He looked at me as if I'd asked his opinion of a black velvet painting of Elvis. "Good heavens, NO!!"

"But you said the paintings were moving, that anyone could see that?"   "AHHH... and that is precisely where the opportunity lies." He glanced up and said softly to himself, "What a masterpiece."

"The Wyeth paintings?"

"No, my column condemning them!"

"But if you liked the paintings why..."

Again, he intercepted my question. "Simply put, my nascent friend, if the critic likes what the public likes, who needs the critic!"

"But haven't you some obligation to the public?"

"My only obligation is to sell newspapers. My column stirs the pot, creates controversy ... and controversy sells. It took months for my phone to settle, people couldn't wait to give me a piece of their minds, not that they could spare it!"

"How did you defend yourself to the callers?"

"Remember public insecurity? I told them it was not my opinion, but their lack of comprehension, that was the problem."

"And if they ask for an explanation of your opinion?"

"There's no use explaining the obvious, it's simply beyond their embrace. Their inner eye is closed."

"Can't the public decide for themselves what constitutes art?"

"Of course they can, but they don't trust themselves. They seek permission; they want to be told. I keep them groping about, insecure, and the more insecure they are, the more they look to me. Put in elemental terms, I tell them that what they think good art is, really isn't, and what they think isn't, really is!"

"It reminds me of a line in the Orwell novel, '1984'," I said. "What's good is bad, what's bad is good."

His eyes narrowed with an arrogant leer. "Slavery is freedom, freedom is slavery," he finished the quote. "Now my friend, you're catching on!"

"All right," I said, "so how do you determine what good art is?"

"Well, there are risks in standing for anything. Security lies in debasement."

"How do you mean?"

"When you oppose something, you make no commitment; you're beyond definition. You exude an aura of superiority."

By now, I didn't have to ask for explanation.

"For example," he said, "let's say I ask you to take me to your favorite restaurant. Instantly, you stake your knowledge, taste and culinary sophistication on your selection of eating establishments. I am automatically placed in the advantageous position of being able to disagree with your selection, therefore placing my culinary knowledge and sophistication above yours. When you endorse, you seek approval. By withholding approval, you claim superiority, and without defining your own view of what quality constitutes."

"But, occasionally, don't you have to commit yourself to some direction?"

"Occasionally, but it is wise to remember that even if your views are acknowledged, fashion soon becomes unfashionable."

"So, what do you do?"

"Seek the bizarre, the exotic, the uninterpretable is open to interpretation, and the assumption of greater sophistication. If the work is beyond translation, you imply a more discerning palette." He gave me a look. "You certainly are the curious sort."

"An opportunity to discuss art with someone of your caliber doesn't come along everyday, I hope you don't mind."

"Have you had an opportunity to explore the galleries and museums in the city?" He was looking for a measure to gauge me by.

"Last year, I saw a watercolor exhibition while I was out here," I said. "I think it was the National Watercolor Society Exhibition."

He bore his picket-fence teeth and let out a queasy squeal. "I dare say, I did a piece on that very exhibition. Local art offers so little challenge."

"Of course, I don't have your expertise, but I must admit I enjoyed the show. Why didn't you like it?"

"I didn't disapprove of the work on a personal level. I merely found little challenge in dissecting the exhibition in my column.   Between us, I find these mongrel exhibitions rather refreshing; however, it would have been critical suicide to say so publicly.   They're far too traditional."

"But, as I recall, the artists represented were from across the country and many of the works were abstract or non-objective."

"Hardly the point, dear boy. Mere non-objectivity went out of vogue with Modern Art."

"How can modern art go out of style?" I asked, and I have to admit, I've always needed a little clarification on that one. "Doesn't the term modern imply the present?"

His goggle eyes glared in exasperation. "Oh dear me, you are provincial. Modern Art is a loose term encompassing a body of work, primarily created in the first half of the 20th century, now, hopelessly out of date."

"So, what period of art are we in now?"

"Post Modernism is the current vogue."

"Aren't those terms self-exclusive?"

"Don't quibble."

"Sorry," I said, as I secretly calculated how many belts could be produced from a hide his size. Out of the corner of my eye, I saw the stewardess strolling back down the aisle. "Excuse me, Miss, could my friend and I have one more drink?"

"Oh Gad, I really mustn't," the creature snarled in protest.

"Just one more," I coaxed. "You can't imagine how valuable this information is to me." The irony of my statement bounced around my brain, flashed by my eyes, and danced out in my tone.

He recoiled in dawning self-awareness. A prickling apprehension blanketed his pasty, pond dwelling face. "I don't believe we've been properly introduced."

"Andrews," I said, "Don Andrews. How do you do?"

"And what, may I ask, is the nature of your business, Mr. Andrews?"

"Me...uh..., I'm a salesman from Toledo."

He lowered his voice and sharpened his pre-historic glare. "I trust any revelations you have ascertained from our conversation will be kept in confidence."

"Oh, don't worry," I smiled, "I won't tell a soul!"

An Unknown Soldier

On lunch break, while teaching in Toronto, several of us were seated in a circle eating our sandwiches. On my left was a lady who spoke to me with an accent I didn't recognize. We made small talk about Toronto, and then she asked me where I was from.

"Alabama," I said.

The name of the state brought a smile to her face and a sparkle to her eyes.

"I must tell you a story," she said.

"I was born in Poland in 1930. I was a child when Germany invaded our country, which marked the beginning of WW II. My father and brothers were killed early in the fighting. My mother and I were sent to a labor camp for the duration of the war. I was fifteen when the war ended with Germany's defeat. The Russian Army liberated us, but they were just as dangerous. Our property was lost and our lives under Russian domination would be little more than slavery.

"We joined a small band of refugees headed westward across Europe, hoping to find passage to Canada, where we had extended family. As we traveled, we would stop to set up camp so that we could rest and eat. We were constantly in fear of the Russian soldiers. There was no authority to restrain them from us, and there were many acts of brutality.

"Whenever possible, we would search out the American lines to camp near, hoping that they would offer us some protection. One night, a few American soldiers came with cans of food and built a fire for us. One of the young soldiers told my mother not to worry about the Russians; he and his friends would protect us from them.

"That night, I stayed up late talking with that soldier by the fire. He had an accent just like yours, and he told me he was from," and she pronounced it, '*Ali-baa-ma*'. "How excited he was that the war had ended and he was going home to marry his sweetheart.

"We passed the night safely and moved on the next day. Finally, we reached the coast and were eventually able to make passage to Canada. It's been my home ever since.

"Whenever I think back on those terrible days, I remember the American boys, and how kind they were to us. As long as my mother lived, she would bless them in her prayers."

I asked her if she remembered the name of the young soldier who brought the cans of food, and she said she was sorry but she didn't.

"Well," I said, "whoever he was, he makes me proud to be a boy from '*Ali-baa-ma!*'"

Hotel Basketball

Usually I enjoy the down time after class, alone in my hotel room. After teaching all day, the quiet can be a comfort, but living out of a suitcase has its downside. Life on the road can get lonesome. Sometimes I feel like a seagull in Kansas. I've used the phrase *'table for one'* more times than I can recall.

When I get to feeling low, I've learned to reach back for memories that keep me grounded. Some say it's not healthy to dwell in the past, but for me it's therapy. It's not the memories of my triumphs and disasters I sift through, but the unexpected moments of insight into the wonderful characters who've touched my life along the way.

The trick to recalling these treasures from the past is to distract myself with some thoughtless activity until something bubbles up in my mind. Like trying to focus on a distant star, I have to look away from it a little for it to come into view. There must be any number of ways to distract yourself when you're alone, but my favorite is, hotel basketball.

I wad a piece of paper into a ball, as tight as I can. Standing across my hotel room at various points and angles, I try to ring the wastepaper basket. It's my version of the old Indian game, put-the-ball-in-the-hole. To add to the excitement, I embellish this activity with dialogue from an imaginary sports announcer barking out the play by play.

"We're down to the final seconds ladies and gentlemen, the underdog Crimson Tide team inbounds the ball to their star forward, Andrews. He'll have to hurry his shot; he turns, he fires...." That's when I throw the paper ball across the room to the wastebasket. It may sound odd, but this mindless endeavor helps clear my mind of my troubles and lets me focus on some distant memory from my past.

Over the last twenty years I've spent countless hours, from one end of this country to the other, playing hotel basketball and, if I say so myself, I'm pretty good at it. In fact, to date, no matter who the opponent or what the odds against me, I've yet to lose.

UNCLE JACK

"Here we are in the waning moments of the regional finals. The ball is brought up court by the opposing team, they're up by one point, the game is all but over, but wait...Andrews steals the ball at half-court, he

throws up a prayer, "Yes!!!!" It's unbelievable... Andrews has done it again...."

I was born and raised in the city of Mobile, but I come from generations of farmers from southeastern Alabama. My mom was a teacher, so most school holidays and a few weeks each summer, she, my brother Bob, and I would make the four hour trek to visit my grandparents and Uncle Jack on their farm near the country town of Ariton. They were poor people by most standards; their portfolio wouldn't impress you. If there was a discussion over the dinner table about some stock to be traded, you can rest assured they were talking about a cow. But their modest country home was lavishly embellished with a tapestry of love for life. Their old formica dinner table with the silver aluminum sides was a silent witness to endless discussions on politics, gossip, and stories laced with laughter. I will forever be proud to be one of them. The Adkinsons were redheaded, raw-boned Irish, lovers of stories and tellers of tales.

From the time my brother Bob and I were old enough to crawl up into the cab of my Uncle Jack's truck, he took us with him on his daily rounds to feed the cattle and hogs, and check on his crops of corn, peanuts and soybeans. Dashboard cluttered with trash, cigarette butts overflowing the ashtray, hot engine fumes blowing up through the holes in the floorboard, my Uncle Jack cracked jokes and sang country songs to the music on the radio. No matter who we passed along the road, Uncle Jack would honk his horn and wave as we rambled by.

Uncle Jack always had his dog Pete along, balanced behind us on the top of the benchseat, barking out the window. My uncle had a variety of lap dogs throughout his life. They all instinctively claimed their spot, perched on top of the seat in his cab and they were all named Pete.

Crammed between boxes of nails, empty sacks of feed, and farm gear, brother Bob and I bounced along beside Uncle Jack, our legs dangling from the seat of his old rusty pickup. For two young city boys, this was a foreign world of fun beyond our wildest dreams.

There was a railroad crossing on the two-lane blacktop road between my grandparents' house and farm. One day as we approached the crossing signs, Uncle Jack downshifted the truck to an idle and came to a complete stop, straddling the rails, with the front wheels of the truck on one side of the tracks and the rear wheels on the other. The cab of the truck was perfectly positioned above the center of the tracks. He shut off the engine and turned to us with a serious look on his face.

"Bob," he said to my brother, "is anything coming down the tracks on your side?"

My brother stood up in the seat and hung out the open window, cupping his eyes to shield them from the blazing summer sun. "No, all's clear!"

"Good," Uncle Jack nodded. "Now, Don, look down this way."

I crawled up over his lap and scanned down the tracks as far as I could see. "Nothing coming," I announced.

"All right," Uncle Jack said as I returned to my seat. "Boys, I promised your mother, today I'd teach you to stop and look both ways before crossing a railroad track!"

AUNT ETHEL

"Andrews is a house of fire tonight, here in room 326 of the Holiday Inn sports complex overlooking the breathtaking panorama of the interstate. He's got the ball again. Looks like he's going to try a 30 footer, the ball is in the air... Incredible, sports fans, he's nailed another one!"

My grandmother's sister was my great Aunt Ethel. She was the matriarch of my mother's family, a grand lady with a domineering presence. Aunt Ethel taught high school in Ariton, Alabama for over forty years, and she didn't just teach in the old school, she was the old school. The doors of the Ariton First Baptist Church were never opened without my Aunt Ethel gracing their entrance. She was the salt of the earth and a force to be reckoned with. Everyone in my family dearly loved Aunt Ethel, but when her car pulled up in the drive, there was a scramble to put out the cigarettes, and hide the bottle. Aunt Ethel did not abide tomfoolery! My Uncle Jack used to say Aunt Ethel could smell liquor on your breath over the telephone!

In the early days of cable television, my mother's sister, my Aunt Cleo, and her husband Floyd purchased a package cable plan that came with a black remote control box to change the channels. Included in the package plan was an adult channel that featured racy movies late at night. Because they had two daughters at home, they had installed a special button on the control box that you could push to scramble reception on just the one channel that featured the bawdy films.

A few years passed, their daughters grew up and went off to college. Aunt Cleo and Uncle Floyd grew lax about scrambling the adult channel on the control box. Aunt Cleo and Uncle Floyd lived in a town an hour or so down the road from Aunt Ethel, and one weekend Aunt Ethel decided to pay a call. They had a good visit the afternoon she arrived, and went out to dinner. Not long after they got back home, Aunt Ethel announced that she was worn from her trip and retired to the spare bedroom that had a television hooked up to cable. An hour or so later, Aunt Cleo and Uncle Floyd went to their bedroom and casually got ready for bed. Suddenly, the potential calamity dawned on Aunt Cleo. She reached over, clawing my uncle's arm, and whispered in exasperation, "Is the reception blocked on the adult channel?"

Floyd looked over in horror to the black box beside the bed. Instantly, he reached out and punched the red button to scramble the adult channel. Anxious minutes ticked by as they sat up in bed pensively hoping they had averted disaster. Then a pounding knock shook their bedroom door; Aunt Ethel's authoritative voice pierced the silence.

"Floyd, come quick," Aunt Ethel commanded. "Something's wrong with the television reception!"

FRANKIE

"There's a hush through the crowd as Andrews steps to the foul line. The game is tied with one second on the clock, the upstart Tide team has pinned its hopes on the back of their freshman sensation, Andrews. The pressure is unbelievable. He steps to the line, he hesitates, the crowd holds its breath, the ball is in the air...Yes, ladies and gentlemen, Andrews saves the day!"

Back in high school, it was the practice of most kids, including my best friend Frankie Fowler and me, to rush into fourth period English class and drop off our books before heading downstairs to the cafeteria for lunch. The English room was on the second floor of our school, and like many un-airconditioned buildings in the Deep South, all the second floor rooms had rows of giant windows, waist-high to the ceiling, which opened out to catch any merciful breeze that happened by.

One day as we rounded the doorway and raced into our English room, there stood Greg Barlow, one of the less sociable characters at our school, standing statue-like, grinning by an open window.

Frankie and I placed our books down on our desks and turned to leave. Still, Greg stood motionless with an expression of delight plastered across his acne-covered face.

"What are you doing, Greg?" Frankie asked, sensing something was up.

"Watch," Greg beamed. Suddenly he rushed over to a vacant desk stacked high with books and scooped them up in his arms. Looking back over his shoulder to make sure no one was coming, he raced to an open window, and in one fluid motion, flung the bundle of books out the window. Then he bowed his back and hung his head out the window to survey the chaos he'd created below. Books and papers fluttered like a flock of unruly pigeons across the schoolyard campus. Thrilled to have an audience, Greg spun back to face us, and his beady eyes gleamed as he raced to gather another stack of books. Frankie knew that Greg's desk was right next to his and when Greg had his back turned to watch the next set of books and papers flutter down, Frankie picked up Greg's books from his desk and scrambled over to him.

"Hurry, Greg!" Frankie shouted. "Throw these out!"

And it is to my everlasting delight that Greg grabbed the books from Frankie's hands, laughing his ugly little laugh, turned, and threw his own books out the window!

"Here we are in the waning moments of the national championship; it's been a real barnburner so far! The Cinderella Crimson Tide team carried by their star Andrews has fought back time and again. Will this be their last hurrah? They're down by one point, Andrews has the ball, he'll take the last shot. He pulls up and fires; the ball is in the air. The whole season is riding on this shot! It's...it's...OHHHHHHH. Just off the rim, it looks like the Tide will be going down in defeat! But wait sports fans... hold everything. I can't believe it; the referee is indicating

that the timekeeper has mishandled the clock! Yes, that's right, there are still two seconds to go! The clock is reset, the ball is once again inbound to Andrews, he'll have to hurry. He launches a bomb from mid-court! The crowd is on its feet, it's, it's...Yes! Yes! He's done it! There's pandemonium, ladies and gentlemen. The crowd is going crazy! Andrews is carried victorious from the court..."

See, I told you I never lose!

Canadians

"You'll be Don, eh?" The man in the passenger seat rolled down his window and said, "Just throw your gear in the back and we'll be off!"

I entered the backseat of the station wagon as the two men up front turned to greet me. Both Bill and James were distinguished-looking older gentlemen. Bill had salt and pepper hair and a sculpted beard, emphasizing the chiseled line of his chin. James's hair had no pepper, but his ready smile and the mischievous twinkle in his blue eyes made him instantly agreeable. They told me they were both enrolled in my landscape workshop being held on Saltspring Island, off the coast of Vancouver.

Tina, the director of the workshop, had escorted the teachers of the other three classes to the island the day before, so she had arranged for James and Bill to give me a ride to the dock and accompany me on the ferry ride to Saltspring Island.

We pulled out of my hotel parking lot onto a busy four-lane boulevard, headed south. While Bill maneuvered into traffic, James turned to me and said, "So, Don, they tell me this is your first trip to Canada, eh?"

"That's right."

"Look sharp," James turned to Bill. "We're practically ambassadors, eh?"

Bill nodded agreement, "Ya know what they say about a first impression, James."

"Just what I was thinking. You see, Don, for over thirty years before we retired, Bill and I worked together as designers in Vancouver, so we practically know what the other is thinking, eh?"

"That's right. Our wives say we should have married each other, and I have to admit, sometimes James here is a bit like a ball and chain, eh?"

"Bill will you stop babbling, and watch the road. We're supposed to take a left on Hawthorne."

"You'll have to excuse James," Bill said as we passed the Hawthorne exit. "It's sad to see age taking its toll on the poor lad."

"Have you not been living in this town the better part of your life? We're going too far south!"

A minute later Bill put on his blinker and we took the next exit, but he circled under the overpass and got back onto the same boulevard we'd been traveling, only now going the other direction. "Now that I've had time to think," Bill said, "perhaps we've gone a bit far, eh?"

James blew out a laugh. "I've been telling you Hawthorne is our turn all morning, but you've always been the stubborn sort, eh?"

"Hawthorne won't get us anywhere," Bill argued as we passed the Hawthorne exit again. "Let's just go up a ways and see what we hit, eh?" While they quibbled, I looked out my left window and saw my hotel go by as we headed in the opposite direction.

"Billy, you simply must take a left if we're to go to the coast!"

"Yes, James, but consider that it's a rather massive coast isn't it, so where we take the left does come into play, eh?"

James's eyes glittered as he sat with his back to the passenger door, talking first to Bill and then to me. "You must be patient, Don. Billy's mind is on the downward slide, eh, it's a terrible thing really!!"

"You know, James," Bill poked his finger in the air, "after further consideration, I do believe Hawthorne will be okay for us after all." He turned his blinker on and again we swung under the overpass and up onto the same boulevard back in our original direction! "Ya see, Don," Bill spoke to me in the rear view mirror, "it's true what they say about a broken clock being right twice a day, eh?"

I looked out my right window as we passed my hotel once again. James's face glowed, obviously delighted with Bill's miscalculations. "It's a lovely first impression you're making, eh? Don said this is his first trip to Canada, but were you planning to show him the entire country this morning?"

Unfazed, Bill turned on his blinker at Hawthorne. "Here we are, just as I thought. I'd have gotten it right the first time if you hadn't distracted me, James!"

"Distracted you! Did ya hear that, Donnie? I distracted him! Bill, would you be so kind as to consider that for the first time since Don has joined us, the sun is in your rearview mirror, giving us some indication that we may finally be headed west, to the coast!"

"Oh, it's so like you isn't it? One minor misstep and like a vulture you descend. It's a sad commentary, Jimmy boy. Don, you'll soon learn that James here is a grouser, no doubt springing from grand insecurities about his failure as an artist!"

"Now, Bill, no sense in misleading the lad. The plain truth is, Don, if I may be allowed to put modesty aside, I'm considered near professional."

Bill's mustache turned up at the corners of his mouth. "Jimmy's pulling your leg now, Don. Indeed the only reason we allow him to come along on these trips is to make the rest of us look better, eh?"

"This is sad, Billy, sad, and you stone cold sober."

This sarcastic swordfight continued unabated as the city of Vancouver gave way to the lush green of fir trees. Thirty minutes later we pulled into a parking lot on the edge of a majestic cove. Down a massive dock rested an elegant alabaster ferryboat. Seagulls banked and stalled on air currents; the scent of saltwater robust in my lungs. People milled about, laden with suitcases and gear. Cars lined up to be loaded onto the aqua-bus.

"Ya know, James, we could off-load our luggage at the end of the dock, park the car and step across the lot to Orcas for a quick one, eh?"

"Grand idea, Bill, the ferry doesn't sail for forty minutes. Donnie here must be parched."

After we'd unloaded our suitcases and parked the station wagon, I followed my two ambassadors across the parking lot to a small bar and grill that hung out over the water. Above the entrance was a huge wooden killer whale holding a sign that read "Orcas." The place was all but empty as I slid into a bench seat across from my two companions.

"Well, Don, what's your pleasure? Billy here is buying, eh?"

"It's a little early for me, guys, I'll just have coffee."

In unison, their cheerful demeanor plummeted. "Did you hear that, James? Donnie here is refusing to have a drink with us. I'm sure you've offended him. Don, please overlook James's crude behavior. I know his manner is coarse, but he's not a bad sort, eh?"

"I just thought we should toast the Queen," James explained. "It's her birthday, eh. You wouldn't refuse a toast to the Queen on her birthday! It's an old Canadian tradition."

Sensing a losing battle, I relented. "Okay, I'll have a Bloody Mary to toast the Queen." The frowns on their faces instantly evaporated and were replaced by the glow of their sunny dispositions.

"That's the ticket, eh. See Bill, Donnie here is a patriot!"

When the waitress appeared, James gave the order. "Miss, may I have two double scotches, blended, and a Bloody Mary please?"

"So is today really the Queen's birthday?"

"It may not be this exact date, but it's within a day or so, eh, surely it must be. The old girl's getting on up there, eh, James?"

When our drinks arrived, James spouted a toast and we all clinked glasses. "Ya see, Don, for many years now James and I have been on the wagon. After a few minor mishaps, really too small to mention, we promised our wives we'd give up the hard stuff for our health and harmony, eh?"

"That's right," James added, "except we stipulated in the agreement that for one week each year during our painting holiday on Salt Spring Island, we would have their permission to indulge."

"Our wives deduced that since we wouldn't have an automobile and we're on an island, as long as we didn't get too close to the water, no great calamity could befall us, eh?"

"No wonder you're in a good mood," I said, "this is your week!"

"We do look forward to our week on Salt Spring. Every year James stands up at our federations annual meeting to propose the workshop be extended for a second week, strictly in the interest of art, eh?"

"I've always been an advocate of education," James said.

"So how are we going to get around on the island?"

"Our friend, Ray, is already on the island," Bill said. "He'll pick us up at the dock and do the chauffeuring all week. The director, Tina, will be there to see about you."

"It sounds like everything is in order for our week of painting together," I said. "Have you both always been interested in art?"

James laughed. "When I first met Bill, he thought *'Lust for Life'* was one of those bawdy books. You've got your hands full with this one, eh?"

Behind the boisterous volume of James' retort, I thought I heard the sound of a foghorn blow. The waitress ambled over to our table.

"You fellows weren't waiting on the ten o'clock to Saltspring, eh?"

Simultaneously, the two of them bolted from the booth. "Come on Don, we best get along, eh?"

As the three of us rounded the door, I looked across the parking lot to see that the loading dock was empty and the line of cars was now pressed on board the ferry. Deckhands were loosening ropes that secured the vessel to the pilings!

"They're taking off!" Bill exclaimed.

Suddenly panic-stricken, I quaked, "Can we make it?"

"We'll have to run for it, eh?" James shouted. Like three aging track stars, we sprinted across the gravel parking lot, grabbed our gear and raced down the dock.

"Hold up," Bill pleaded with the deck crew. Suitcases and portfolios sailing through the air, we jumped from dock to deck. A numbing blast from the foghorn buffeted the air and the giant double-decker vessel churned away from its mooring!

Ears pulsing, chest heaving, I bent over to catch my breath. Bill leaned on the gunwale beside me. "Nothing like a brisk stroll to wet your thirst, eh, James?" he huffed!

Clinging on the railing, sucking in oxygen, "Right you are, Billy," James spouted between gulps. A few minutes later we lumbered up metal steps following signs to the snack bar. Bill and I claimed a small varnished table nestled beneath life preservers and took our seats. James purchased three soft drinks with extra ice, then sashayed to the side rail. One by one, he held his hand over the mouth of the cups, and poured the soft drinks over the side.

Joining us at the table with the cups of ice, he craned his head over both shoulders in clandestine fashion. Unzipping his carry bag, he produced a small bottle, refilled each cup with liquid and passed the cups around.

"Have ya ever noticed," James said, his eyes twinkling like diamonds, "some of the most exhilarating moments of your life were directly preceded by the words, we'll have to run for it, eh?"

An hour later, our ferry maneuvered up to its mooring on Saltspring Island. A cool mist rising from shimmering waters equalized the first warm rays of the summer sun. James, Bill and I sauntered down the catwalk onto the main deck, collected our bags and with careful measurement, stepped onto the dock. There to greet us was a nice looking man and woman who shook our hands and grabbed some of our bags.

"What did I tell you, eh," Ray smiled to Tina. "They're half-wrecked already!"

In the parking lot I was led to Tina's car. James and Bill loaded their bags in Ray's truck. We said our goodbyes and drove away. "I hope your trip over with those two went all right, eh?" Tina voiced her concern as we drove to my room. I reassured her and then I asked if the story they told me about only drinking one week each year on Saltspring Island was true.

"It's absolutely true, but don't worry. Ray will be watching out for them and he'll make sure they get to your class each day. Most of your other students have been with them on Saltspring before, so they know what to expect. They can be a little disruptive, but they're both wonderful guys. In past years everyone in class enjoyed their antics!"

Tina paused to measure my reaction. "They'll be fine," I said.

"Oh, I'm sure, but if there's any problem, you will let me know, eh?"

The next morning amid the chaos of students setting up their painting gear, James and Bill swayed into the studio. Everyone laughed and shouted mock complaints as the two of them gathered greetings and hugs around the room. They were pointed to a table right up front that had a cardboard sign with their names printed on it. Just behind them, Ray came through the door loaded with painting gear and deposited it on their table.

"Alright, you two can set up your own gear, eh?" Then Ray turned and gave me a wink. "These guys shouldn't be any trouble. They were up all night playing bum-darts!"

"Huh?"

"I'll explain later," he said, "but if you need me, I'm just next door in Kiff's class, eh?"

At nine o'clock the class was assembled in semi-circle rows of chairs for my introduction and morning lesson. James and Bill sat right up front, reverent as deacons, and not the slightest hint of trouble. They were attentive, silent and studious. When I finished, the class adjourned and students returned to their desks to begin painting. As always some people chatted awhile or stopped for a cup of coffee, but within ten minutes the clamor settled down to silence. Immersed in their work for the next hour, Bill and James were sterling examples of model students.

Suddenly, Bill's booming voice rocked the studio and the heads of the entire class jerked to attention. "James, please excuse me for asking, but I can stand it no longer. Pray tell, why are you painting that airplane flying into a fir tree, eh?"

The volume of James' response was equally impressive. "That's not an airplane," he shouted defensively, "it's an eagle!"

"An eagle!" Bill exclaimed as if he were shocked beyond belief. " That's a sad eagle, eh?"

"Sad you say, and what exactly is so sad about my eagle?"

"Jimmy boy, have ya never heard the word aerodynamics?"

"You're a fine one to talk, eh. Here we've spent all this time and trouble getting to the coast, and there you sit painting some sort of toxic waste dump!"

"Are you mad? This is a sunset on Mt. Baker, and it's shaping up nicely if I may say so!"

James' eyes sparkled, his face a pink flush, he shook his head and jeered, "Poor Billy, it looks like one of those atomic meltdown scenes that foretell Armageddon!"

"I'll have you know, I am producing this masterpiece only after meticulous hours of observation on our balcony, studying the sunset on Mt. Baker, eh?"

"Not to put too fine a point on it, Billy," James taunted, "first, you can't see Mt Baker from our balcony. Second, you were bagged long before the sun thought about setting last night, and third, the only time you came close to the balcony, was to relieve yourself, eh?"

By now every member of our class had put down their brushes and were laughing hysterically! Tears running down James' red cheeks, he looked up at me and smiled.

"Once again, I must apologize for my friend, Bill. Perhaps now ya see what you're dealing with, eh?"

The next morning Ray delivered James and Bill to class right on time. Glassy eyes blinking, arms dangling and heads nodding, they sat stoic as Mounties through my lesson and demo. They seemed to catch their second wind after the mid-morning break and for the rest of the morning they were industrious mutes.

It must have been around two o'clock when Bill's booming voice engulfed the studio. "I must say it, James, I

154

really must! Poor Don has spent the better part of the morning giving a lovely lesson on color theory. Now what is he to think of the disaster on your paper, eh? It's absolutely monochromatic!"

"I must protest," James shouted back, "there is a definite spot of blue here in the upper corner, is there not?"

"Did you hear that everyone? James, what a risk taker you've become, a real daredevil! Everybody, come see! James has really made a breakthrough, eh?"

"This is a little hard to take after all the help I've given you over the years," James countered. " I'm sure everyone will love your painting depicting space creatures walking down the beach, eh?"

"Are you daft, those are figures!" Bill bristled as if outraged. "They're not quite right yet, but give me a chance. I'm still working, eh?"

"Not quite right! It looks like Martians invading Normandy! Everyone, come see Bill's illustration for a science fiction movie, eh!"

"There you go, Jimmy, I've never known anyone so eager to show his ignorance!"

"Ignorance! Ya don't have to go to art school to know that a head has two eyes on it, eh?"

"This one has two eyes," Bill pointed to his painting.

"Yes, Billy, but do consider that with human anatomy, the eyes are not generally found on the same side of the head, eh?"

Wednesday morning, James and Bill came dragging through the door just as I was calling the class to order.

Squinting eyes, baggy and crimson, with sleepy smiles they greeted me and took their usual seats. I hadn't given five minutes of my presentation before they both nodded off and fell sound asleep. Forty minutes later I finished the demonstration and opened up the lesson to questions. They began to stir as the question and answer period concluded and the class dispersed. The rumble of chatter around them brought James and Bill out of their slumber, and with groggy expressions, they slowly stumbled up to me. Bill gave me an appreciative pat on the shoulder.

"Grand job, Donnie boy. It's a pleasure to watch a professional work, eh, James?"

"Right you are, Billy! It's a sign of a master who makes it all look easy, eh?"

"Indeed, James. Now let's hope that you'll be able to utilize a small portion of the information Don has provided to improve that monstrosity on your easel, eh?"

"That's an insult and I resent it," James barked. "And what would you call space creatures storming on shore, eh? I dare say you've frightened some of the ladies!"

Thursday morning Bill swayed through the doors of our studio at two minutes till nine. Up to my table he wobbled, a somber smile turning up the mustached corners of his handsome gray beard.

"Sorry, Don, James is a little under the weather this morning, eh? Poor devil sends his regrets. I hope you won't think badly of him. He wouldn't miss your class for the world, but he's having a touch of indigestion, eh?" He gave me a wink. "I'll catch him up on the lesson."

I assured Bill I understood, and then he reeled around and sauntered to his seat. I went ahead with the lesson, and when the demo was done, the class settled into what promised to be a comparatively quiet morning.

The following hour of silence came to an abrupt halt when the studio doors swung open and the squinting, tottering figure of James staggered in. He gave me a wave of acknowledgment and took his place at his desk next to Bill.

For a minute, James sat oscillating silently in his seat until Bill looked over at him and boomed, "Well, aren't you a sight, Jimmy. Just look at ya, eh?"

In slow motion James raised a finger to pursed lips and blew out a hush. "Not so loud, Billy, take a little pity, eh?"

Bill drew himself up and blasted full bore, "Oh, it's pity ya want, eh? Here we are trying to improve ourselves and in you come, half bagged, looking for pity!"

"Sorry, Bill," James spoke with a sheepish smile. "I think I've got a touch of the flu."

"The flu! You've got a touch of flu no doubt. The vodka flu, eh? Lucky for you, I took a few notes to catch you up."

"You took a few notes?"

"A few. I thought I might need them in case some day I decide to take on students myself, eh?"

Upon hearing Bill's declaration, you could see James' brows arch. That old familiar light once again sparkled in his bloodshot eyes. "Students," he blinked as if trying to comprehend, "*you*, taking on students!" his voice dripping with sarcasm. "Oh, Billy, pity the poor students, eh?"

An electric buzz floated about the class Friday morning as the group gathered for my lesson. James stood up to announce there was a Saltspring tradition that all students stout-hearted enough to have survived the four classes, meet after dinner for a send-off celebration. Bill produced a map directing everyone through a small wooded grove that lead to a covered picnic pavilion overlooking an inlet, where the festivities were to commence. I didn't want to say anything in front of the class about a possible glitch I could foresee, so I waited until after the lesson to amble over to their table. Before I could open my mouth, James spoke up.

"Don, just the man we needed to see. Bill, Ray and I are having a little cookout for dinner tonight and we insist that you join us. We can all go to the party together from there, eh?"

I didn't want to throw a wet blanket on the party, but I reminded them that the three of us had tickets for the seven a.m. ferry back to the mainland the following morning. They were then supposed to drive me to the airport.

"Not to worry," James assured me, "most everyone's heading out tomorrow so the party won't run late. Ray is planning on driving us all to the ferry in the morning, so we're sure to be on time, eh?"

My fears allayed, I accepted their invitation and we turned our attention back to art. The day proceeded smoothly as the class fell into silent pursuit of that one last workshop painting. It wasn't until late afternoon when the group's collective concentration was rattled back to reality by Bill's boisterous proclamation!

"Good heavens, James, now you've done it! That's a grand disaster, eh?"

James looked wounded. "I wouldn't expect you to appreciate it. It's experimental. I'm trying to express my inner feelings, eh?"

"Express your inner feelings! Jimmy lad, if that's an example of your inner feelings, may I suggest you seek medical attention!"

James tried to hide his smile, standing with arms folded on his chest. "You shouldn't attack things simply because you don't understand them, Billy. This work is modern, symbolic; it must be studied to be appreciated."

"You've got me there. I'd need a belt before I'd comprehend the meaning of that thing."

" Perhaps a few jiggers of whisky would be beneficial to loosen you up so you could appreciate true artistic symbolism."

"My dear James, I dare say there is not enough whisky in Ireland to make me appreciate the symbolism in the catastrophe you have before you!"

"Poor Billy, I know I'm asking a great deal of you but take a second look at my painting and keep an open mind. Tell me, what inner urges manifest themselves, eh?"

"Since you put it that way, James, I do believe I'm beginning to understand! At this very moment I have an overwhelming inner urge to find a box of matches!"

"Oh, Billy, you really couldn't show your ignorance more openly if ya ran up and down the hall proclaiming the fact! You might consider while you're having your laugh, that perhaps my creation is simply too elevated for your rudimentary comprehension, eh?"

"Too elevated is it! I'd wager an astronaut's not elevated enough to comprehend the meaning of that monstrosity! And since the possibility of a sale is nonexistent, do tell me, dear James, what you plan to do with that thing, eh?"

James puffed up like a peacock. "I'm glad you asked. I was just thinking I'd take a slide to send Don to use in his brochure, as an example of the work his students create in his workshop."

Bill's face contorted. "Are you mad, James? The mailing of that brochure would instantly mark the demise of poor Donnie's career!"

A short time later, the class settled back down. We all complimented each other on our week's work and agreed to save our goodbyes until the party.

After class, I lugged my paint gear back to my room and got ready for the evening's festivities, the vast majority of which, will forever remain a mystery to me.

The beginning and ending of the evening are, at best, vaguely etched in my mind's eye. There are nebulous flashes of recall that form only at the corners of my memory! I do vividly remember arriving at my three hosts' cabin for a cookout. James said he'd be honored to fix me a drink. I accepted his hospitality and was presently served a Flintstones jelly jar filled to the crest with vodka on the rocks.

"James, go easy, the night is young!"

"Not to worry," he reassured me, "it's mostly ice!"

From there, my recollection of events becomes hazy at best! I do remember stepping over a small brook as we stumbled through sloping woods to get to the waterfront picnic pavilion, where a multitude of artists had gathered. There are postcard flashes in the peripheral part of my mind of merriment, jokes, laughter and people spontaneously breaking out in song! I think I won a game of bum-darts. I vaguely recall someone telling me a couple of times not to worry, it was mostly ice, and I'm pretty sure I took a pledge to become a Canadian citizen! Then, there's a lot of blank tape until Ray tapped me on the shoulder, pointed to his watch and began shepherding James, Bill and me back up the wooded hill.

The tiny brook had been easy enough to negotiate on our descent to the party some hours before. However, sunlight had now transformed to moonbeams, and our footing wasn't so steady!

Even for a stream, the waterway wasn't impressive, no more than an inch or so deep. The brook babbled over peanut-sized pebbles as it flowed its final mile before reaching the Strait of Georgia.

"AAAUUUHHHEEE!!!"

Just ahead of me came a cry, instantly followed by a splash! I stumbled up through darkness and saw the shadowed silhouette of James lying motionless, face up, on his back in the brook. He appeared as if he was lying comfortably in his favorite bed.

No sooner had I arrived than Ray and Bill came up beside me, and we all knelt around James as he lay there. A serene smile graced his lips, and the twinkle in his eyes reflected the light of the moon. His right arm crooked up at the elbow, securing a Flintstones glass above the water. We took turns inquiring about injuries, but James wasn't vaguely interested in our concerns. Nor did it appear that he was in any discomfort. In fact, he seemed quite pleased to find a refreshing spot to take a break!

"It's a lovely night to view the stars, lads," he smiled up at us and said, his face a picture of peaceful tranquility. "You can see Orion's belt just over there, eh?"

With a good deal of effort we managed to pull him to his wavering feet. James looked down at his cartoon glass and held it up in triumph. "Never spilled a drop, eh?"

A few minutes later we arrived at my door. Ray looked down at his watch and then to me. "We'll have to be at the ferry in a little less than six hours, eh?"

"I'll be ready," I mumbled. Then I poured myself from the cab of the truck.

I slapped off the shrieking alarm and struggled to a seated position on the side of the bed. In exactly one hour, the 7 o'clock ferry would be pulling away from its mooring and heading back to the mainland! The demons in my head cackled at the aspirin I choked down before I staggered around my room, packing clothes and paint gear. With unsteady steps, I threw my luggage in a pile outside my door and sat down on them to rest while I waited for my ride. Blinking my eyes till they focused, I looked down at my watch. It now read 6:45. For six minutes I tottered on my seat of luggage, head pounding, counting down the time.

Suddenly, from around the corner, a truck containing three rag-doll figures bounded up to me!

"Let's hurry, eh?" Ray shouted as he jumped from the cab to help me load up. I opened the passenger door and sandwiched James and Bill into the middle of the bench seat. They grunted greetings as Ray jerked the truck into gear. Tires spewing gravel, we catapulted into motion! Swerving and swaying, the truck sliced through the early morning mist. Adrenalin pumped me into semi-consciousness, as seconds ticked by in our frenzied race to beat the clock! James and Bill were mute as mummies as they bounced along beside me. Rounding one final turn we accelerated into the entrance to the ferry parking lot.

A blast from a marine foghorn brought James and Bill to some semblance of life. Our truck raced up to the edge of the dock leading to the ferry's gangplank, as two deckhands unleashed giant ropes that secured the vessel. Waiting for the truck to grind to a halt, I shouted out to anyone who might answer, "Can we make it?" I turned and caught a glimpse of James' pink face as he slouched beside me. There was a hint of a twinkle sparkling in his bloodshot eyes. "I don't know," he said, "we'll have to run for it, eh?"

Mexican Food

"Don, let me take you out to dinner."

"Thank you, but after class on Mondays, all I want to do is go back to my hotel and rest."

"But where will you eat?

"Oh, I'll grab a bite in the hotel restaurant."

"You don't mind eating alone?"

"No, no, I'll be fine."

"Well, when you do go out to eat, what kind or restaurant do you like?"

" I'm not particular, but I am partial to Mexican."

"If you'll change your mind, I know a great little Mexican restaurant not five minutes from your hotel."

"I'm sure it's good but I'm not that hungry yet and what I really want is to put my feet up."

"Of course, you're tired after teaching all day, but you've got to eat, and this place is special. We could just pop in before the crowd."

"It's that good, huh…"

"Everyone says so…"

"Well, I guess I could eat something."

"Now I feel like I've forced you. We don't have to go if you're tired."

"Really, it's okay."

"No, you said you're tired, so we'll go another time."

"I suppose another time would be better. I'll take a rain check."

"But now you'll have to eat hotel food; it can't be very good."

"Oh, I don't mind it. Besides, I'm not really dressed to go out."

"If that's all you're worried about, no one will care; it's casual. I tell you what, let's just drive by and see if this place is open. What do you say?"

"Sounds good."

"You know, now that I think of it, I know they don't open until 5:30 or 6:00."

"In that case I'll just go back to my room, catch my breath, and have dinner a little later."

"No, no, I can tell you have your heart set on a Mexican dinner. I tell you what, I know a Mexican place that's open all day, but it's a little drive. Do you want to?"

"If it's that good, then let's go."

"Great! So, Don, I didn't know you were crazy for Mexican food."

"Oh sure, every time I come out west, I try to have as much as I can."

"Well, you'll like this place; it's really well known."

"Oh yeah? What's it called?"

"Taco Bell!"

Ellen

There is no advantage in knowing how you're going to die. I don't want to be gruesome, but there's an excellent chance I'll be killed in an automobile accident while having an invigorating conversation with someone whose job for the week is to deliver me to a workshop, airport or hotel.

I've tried over the years to postpone this event by becoming a backseat driver, but you can only do so much. It's just a matter of time.

In my sleepy little hometown, there are two red lights and maybe four or six stop signs. People actually yield the right of way; I've seen it happen. Perhaps I'm not accustomed to road travel in the more accelerated areas of the country. I always thought New Orleans was bad, until I went to New York, until I went to LA, until I was picked up by Ellen.

I'd arrived at my hotel by shuttle bus from the airport in San Francisco. That night, I got a call from a lady with a pleasant voice who introduced herself as Ellen. She told me her job for the week was to pick me up and deliver me to and from our workshop each day. Ellen said she'd be by at 8:00 in the morning for a 30-minute drive to class. I asked her what make of car she drove so I could be on the lookout for her. She laughed and told me not to worry. I couldn't miss her.

The next morning, surrounded by paint gear and portfolio, I stood waiting outside my hotel. Up rattled an ancient two-tone VW van, covered with dents, rust and bumper stickers. Out popped a stout lady in a blue denim skirt and dotted tennis shoes. Ellen introduced herself, grabbing my hand and pumping it firmly. Then she snatched open the side door of the van.

"Let me help you with your gear," she said as she pushed back folding chairs, frames, a spotlight and boxes of assorted junk. We jammed my portfolio and easel in the van and slammed the door shut. I opened the passenger door, moved the clutter of palettes, books, brushes, and assorted art materials from the passenger seat to the floorboard and hopped in. Ellen entered from the driver's side and handed me a cup of coffee. With the turn of a key, the sputtering engine coughed to life.

She turned to me and shouted, "If my driving scares you, tell me, and I'll let you take over!" She was smiling as she said it, but from past experience, when you get advance notice, it's not a good sign! I returned her smile, having not the slightest idea where we were, where we were headed or how to get there.

"I'll chance it," I screamed above the noise of the unmuffled engine.

"Good luck!" Ellen replied. With that, she popped the clutch. My head snapped back, hot coffee flying, paint gear and folding chairs crashing behind us. Books and papers slid across the floorboard at my feet. Rat-a-tat-tatting away we shot, in a cloud of blue exhaust.

For three blocks, we weaved through mangled suburban traffic, Ellen gunning the engine, racing up behind cars, turning around in her seat to check for a clear lane. We swerved first into the left lane, raced ahead, and then cut hard into the right. My waistline pinched against my seat belt as centrifugal force pulled me back and forth. Ellen, nonchalantly chatted all the while.

"So, Don, why did you move up to New Hampshire…Oh come on mister, now just where do you think you're going? Oh, Don, I didn't know if you take your coffee with… AHHHH…Lady! Some people!" As we approached a light, it changed to red and the brake lights of the car ahead of us flashed. Easels and paint gear crashed. Books, palettes and pencils flew back across my feet in the opposite direction. We screeched to a halt. Motionless, and a little stunned, we sat waiting for the light to change. Ellen looked over to me and announced, "We'll take the freeway up ahead. It's faster!"

A block later, she swatted her blinker on, we swerved hard right, and Ellen downshifted with grinding gears. We gained momentum and slung-shot our way onto eight lanes of California interstate.

"Don't worry," she said, "We'll be right on time!"

She punched the accelerator. We whipped across a few lanes at breakneck speed. Horns blared around us as we fishtailed and then straightened up in the far left lane.

"How do you like Central California, Don?" Ellen yelled.

"So far," I shouted, "it's pretty exciting!"

We seemed to be settling into our trip. I thought I'd take a chance and have a sip of what was left of my coffee, not that I needed extra stimulation. One thing was obvious. If we made it to class, I'd be awake when we got there!

Another thing was becoming clear. Ellen had a habit of turning her head to make eye contact when she talked. She would glance at the road on occasion, but it didn't seem to be a high priority. "Don," she shouted, "we're so happy to have you here. Everyone's been looking forward to painting with you this week!"

Even with my heart in my throat, I couldn't help but like Ellen. She was on time to pick me up, and brought me a cup of coffee. Besides, anyone who looks forward to my teaching can't be all bad. In California, everybody drives like a maniac, so we were blending nicely with the traffic flow.

We passed spaghetti-like overpasses, through a corridor of bald hills that glowed gold in the morning sun. Ellen asked if I was at all familiar with artists from California. I told her some of my biggest influences were painters of the California School. I'd grown up studying their work with color and light.

"Millard Sheets was my favorite teacher," Ellen said.

"You studied with Millard Sheets?"

"Many times," she said, "and George Post and of course, Rex and Joan." I was about to ask her to tell me about them, when my train of thought was severed by her shout, "OOPS!" as she slapped on her blinker and slammed on the brakes. Downshifting, we sliced hard to the right, cutting across three lanes. "Almost missed our turn." Horns blared, cars swerved and tires screamed. With all my strength, I clutched the door handle to keep in my seat, as we zipped up the exit ramp. Again, she downshifted, and again, paint gear crashed around me. My seat belt dug into my middle as we came to a smoking halt at the intersection red light.

I exhaled, trying to regain composure as a car filled with young men, pulled up in the lane next to us. Ellen's window was rolled up but they were really letting us have both barrels, hand signals flying, rough language filling the air. Ellen was half facing me, chatting away, when she stopped mid-sentence, excused herself, and began rolling down her window to a volley of vulgarity.

"Hey, you old _____, why don't you watch where you're _____ going!"

"Young man," Ellen said, completely unruffled.

"_____ lady, are you _____ crazy?"

"Young man," Ellen replied, "I'm *so* sorry if I inconvenienced you."

"Are you kidding lady, you _____ near…"

Ellen cut him off. "Dear me, I can't tell you how sorry I am."

Finally he relented. "Look lady, it's okay, just try to be more careful."

"Oh, thank you, young man," Ellen cooed. "I'll try!"

Ellen rolled up her window, turned and gave me a wink. "Little shits fall for it every time!" With that she swatted the steering wheel, burst out with a wonderful throaty laugh, and off we went again.

I'm happy to report that we did make it to class that day, and class went well. In California, I expect the quality of the artists in the workshop to be high. Californians are exposed to such good artwork of all tastes and directions. Several times that day I stopped to admire Ellen's painting. In it was a strength that comes only with a lot of hard work. Ellen wasn't just a good painter; she was a good person to have in class. She was upbeat and kind, constantly encouraging the artists around her.

That afternoon as I climbed into the old van for the drive back to my hotel, I was a little tired, but I felt good about the day's proceedings. I always say, a workshop is divided into two halves, Monday, and the rest of the week, and Monday had gone well.

"So, Ellen, when did you start painting?"

Ellen turned the key, grinding down gears as the old engine rattled to life.

"Oh, it's a long story."

I buckled my seatbelt and pulled it snug. "Think of me as a captive audience."

"You might say I traded my ex-husband, Frank, for my art."

"You'll have to explain that one."

"When I was young," Ellen began, "I wanted more than anything to become an artist. California was brimming with new directions in painting, new attitudes about art, and the relationship of art to society. It was all so exciting. It was a great time to be young in California. My junior year at Claremont I met Frank, one thing led to another, you know the story. We got married, and I got pregnant. Well, it didn't take long before Frank began to complain that my painting was getting in the way of the important things in life. Frank turned out to be one of those control freaks. He thought silent children were good children, a wife's place was in the kitchen." Ellen rolled her eyes.

"Frank set himself up as judge and jury in our lives. It was our job to please him, and he was never satisfied. We never could live up to Frank's expectations. As the kids got older, he began to bully them. I was afraid they would grow up tentative, unsure of themselves, as I had become. It got to the point that Frank openly criticized all my work, constantly complaining about the cost of classes and materials. When I told him my sales more than covered the expense, he said if I didn't waste time painting, I could clean the house properly!

" Just when I thought my life in art was over, fate lent a hand! I was getting a little older; my figure wasn't what it was before I had four children. One day, Frank announced that he had found someone who understood him. Ha!" Ellen laughed. "She was barely voting age. After Frank moved out, I had myself a good cry, until it dawned on me that I finally had control of my life. I was better off without some egomaniac to kowtow to! Money was tight, but we always managed, and our house grew loud with laughter. How exciting life became without Frank. I could make my own decisions, and I decided I was going to follow my art."

" Ellen," I said, "that's just great!"

Ellen jutted her jaw, her face a silhouette in the late afternoon sun. "Oh, it gets better," she said. "After Frank had been with sweet-thing for a few years, he showed up at my door wanting me to take him back. The idiot had the nerve to ask me if I ever thought of him when I went to bed at night!"

"What did you say?"

"I said, I sure do Frank. Nothing puts me to sleep faster than the thought of you!" With that Ellen swatted the steering wheel and let go with that wonderful gravelly laugh.

The next morning, Ellen's van rattled up to my hotel curb right on time. As I entered, she gave me a "Good Morning" greeting and handed me a cup of coffee. It had one of those plastic lids on it, and this time I waited until we got to the interstate before I opened it up.

"Ellen," I said as we rifled along, "I couldn't help but notice a bumper sticker on the front of your van that reads, "Visualize World Peace" right next to one with a picture of a pistol that says, "I don't call 911."

Ellen yelled above the engine roar. "Oh, the mood swings these days!"

After I'd finished the painting demonstration that morning, Ellen came up to me and asked if my demos were for sale on time payment. Selling my paintings is always awkward, and I'm pretty sure I can talk anyone out of buying one. I've learned over the years to keep my comments simple. I said, "My demos are always for sale over time."

Pointing to the painting, Ellen declared, "Sold."

After class that afternoon, as we entered the van, Ellen said, "I know you must be tired and want to go back to your room to put your feet up, but if you'd like to stop by my house for a drink, I can show you my painting collection." As if to up the ante, she added, "I've got a Millard Sheets!" Ellen was right, I was tired, my feet did hurt, but with the offer of a drink and Millard Sheets, I couldn't say no!

Presently, we zoomed through a modest, well-kept neighborhood lined with Eucalyptus trees. Perhaps it was my imagination, but I swear the neighborhood dogs and cats would up and run for cover as they heard our unmuffled van approach. Without warning or much slowing down, we turned hard and bounced into the driveway of a handsome little home. Stonework and woodcarving accented a small entryway overflowing with bougainvillea. Ellen unlatched a hand carved hardwood door, and we stepped into a living room that could rival most museums.

For a moment, I stood speechless. There, on the walls around me was a vast collection of watercolor paintings from the California School. There must have been fifty of them; Phil Dike, Jade Fon, Rex Brandt, George Post, Joan Erving, Milford Zornes, Phil Paradise, Barse Millar, Robert E.Wood and yes, there, in the corner with one of those little museum lights above it, was a Millard Sheets' landscape. All my heroes in one room! Ellen didn't intrude as I stumbled, gawking in slow motion, around the room. There would be time for talk, but first I wanted to quietly take it all in. My feet no longer hurt, I wasn't tired. Ellen let me go in silence. She seemed to disappear. After I'd started my second go-around, Ellen reappeared.

"What a marvelous collection!" I said.

Ellen handed me a glass of wine and threw out her arms with pride. "Fifty dollars a month for life!"

Wednesday morning started well enough. Ellen arrived right on time and handed me a cup of coffee as I entered the van. We had what I thought was an uneventful three blocks to our exit. I was beginning to think I was getting used to Ellen's driving. I anticipated and pre-positioned myself for the slingshot method of entering the interstate. A defensive horn or two sounded, but once we staked out our position in the far left lane, for a few miles nothing much happened. Then Ellen grew silent as she pointed through the windshield at a small building reflecting the morning sunlight on top of a massive golden hill.

"Don, how would you paint that?" Totally absorbed in her own question, she was slowly turning herself to her side window as we passed the building. Doing so, she turned the wheel slightly and our van began to drift. A horn honked behind us. Ellen jolted and whipped us back into our lane. "Sorry Mister," she waved into her rearview mirror. Then she turned to face me. "People say I'm the worst driver they've ever ridden with, what do you think?"

"You've gotta be a contender," I smiled.

"Thank goodness most people are good sports and just naturally get out of my way."

"I'll bet they do."

"Of course, when worse comes to worse," she said, "I've got a finger too!"

"Do you ever have any run-ins with the police?"

"Oh my, yes," Ellen laughed, "but usually they're nice and let me off with a warning. Not long ago, though, I was on a museum paint-out with a van full of kids, when a policeman stopped me. He was one of those tough-guy, reflector sunglasses types. He strutted up to my window and shouted in my face, ' I've got a good mind to throw you in jail.'" Ellen set her jaw as she recounted the scene, "I yelled right back, 'Good! Then you can take care of this van full of screaming kids!'"

"So what happened?"

Ellen gave me a wink. "Oh, he let me go!"

The next morning, as we wove snake-like through a maze of unsuspecting candidates for rear-end collision, the topic of conversation landed on one of my favorites. I'd just married a girl with four children, and to my surprise, I'd suddenly become rich.

"So, Don, how do you like living with four kids?"

"I feel like the luckiest man alive, when I'm not pulling my hair out!"

Ellen grinned. "I'm not sure if they give life meaning," she said, "but they sure make it interesting."

"Yeah, they do."

"One time," Ellen said, "my four youngsters and I were getting ready to go somewhere. I was ranting and raving, trying to get all the last-second things done, while refereeing total chaos. In between my yelling, I was trying to take my vitamins. I got so flustered that I took the dog's heartworm pill by mistake."

As Ellen relayed her story, little by little she began to shift toward me in her seat. I tried to concentrate on what she was saying, but I couldn't help noticing she was almost completely facing me as she talked. Ellen propped a casual hand on top of the steering wheel, her glances at the road ahead becoming less and less frequent.

We were in the left lane of a four-lane boulevard. Up ahead of us was a car, stopped in our lane, with its' blinker on, waiting to make a left turn. "So I called the doctor," Ellen howled, "and he told me he couldn't help. I'd have to call my vet! Ha, Ha..." Ellen slapped her thigh as she laughed.

Dividing my focus between Ellen and the upcoming obstacle; my head jerked back and forth. Ellen had been facing me for some time and I hoped she was due to take a glance at the road. My feet pressed harder and harder into the floorboard, my back arched out my seat. My hands clenched the armrest. I could see the car ahead wasn't going to have an opening to turn before we got to it.

Meanwhile, Ellen was completely engrossed in her story and having a great time. I had to do something and I had to do it now, the car was upon us!

"Ellen!" I shouted, as I pointed bug-eyed to the windshield. Ellen glanced forward, and in that instant, effortlessly turned the steering wheel. We swerved into the right-hand lane, sailing past the stationary obstacle without the slightest reduction in speed.

Adrenaline ballooning the veins of my temples, my pulse was banging like a hammer on an anvil. Ellen again turned the steering wheel and we swerved right back into the left lane, her story suffering not the slightest interruption. "So I called the vet," she shouted, "and he said, 'nothing to worry about, Ellen, as long as you're still over forty pounds!' Ha, Ha, Ha!"

That night as I lay on my hotel bed, replaying the day's near-disaster, I came to several conclusions about Ellen. First, I really liked her. She was considerate, talented and possessed a wonderfully witty, fertile mind. However, conversation with Ellen was equally delightful and dangerous. It seemed she absolutely forgot she was behind the wheel of a two thousand pound projectile when she was engaged in thought. As long as she faced forward as she drove, and the conversation was contained to observation, we were relatively safe. It was when she reminisced on some story and began turning in her seat, that signaled danger. The trick to survival, I decided, was not to end conversation, but redirect it.

Friday morning, I stood out front of my hotel. As usual, Ellen came rolling up with my "good morning" smile and cup of coffee. Alert with the anxiety of the unknown, I buckled and took a defensive posture, instantly putting my survival plan into action as we pulled out into traffic.

"My goodness, isn't that an unusual color for a truck? What exactly causes fog anyway? Do hummingbirds think those red flower feeders are gaudy?" The quality of conversation suffered, but my strategy proved sound. We made it to class with only a few near disasters.

Friday is always a good day in a workshop. You may be tired, but it's a good tired. I had genuinely enjoyed the week with the group. At the end of the day, we packed up our paint gear, and said our good-byes. In the parking lot, Ellen and I crammed the van with art materials, portfolios, and easels and slammed the side door shut. As I buckled myself into the passenger seat, I tried to mentally prepare for our last ride together. Ellen cranked the engine and turned to face me. We were still stationary, but like Pavlov's dog, I tensed up anyway.

"If one more person tells me Mark Twain said the coldest winter he ever spent, was a summer in San Francisco," she said, " I think I'm gonna scream!" With that wonderful hearty laugh, Ellen swatted the steering wheel and popped the clutch. My head snapped back as tires screeched and paint gear crashed. One last time, in a cloud of blue exhaust, we were off!

Mile after mile we traveled, my hands twitching with anticipation as I mindlessly chatted away. Onto the interstate we swerved, slingshot style. Like a sentry, I cranked my head around, surveying oncoming traffic for imminent danger, but so far our luck was running. "Wasn't Amy a good model?" I babbled.

"Oh yes," Ellen said. "Remember when we were young and our skin fit?"

For a moment, I was in fear of an oncoming story, but Ellen's laughter subsided, and she hardly glanced over. Phew! I thought to myself, false alarm!

A few miles later, Ellen slapped her turn signal on and we catapulted off the interstate onto the boulevard that had been the scene of yesterday's near calamity. I strained my eyes and craned my neck, but I saw no obstructions; no one was turning, our lane was clear, our luck was holding! Moment by moment, mile by mile, unscathed, we drew closer to our destination. Perhaps it was with that realization that I made a critical error. I began to get my hopes up. We were within blocks of my hotel. Yes! We were going to make it! It was springtime in California, birds were singing, flowers blossomed and I was going to live!

Ellen turned ever so slightly to me in her seat. "Speaking of kids," she said, her sparkling eyes looking into mine. My mind raced, I tried to cut her off, but it was already too late. "A few years back," Ellen beamed, "I took a class in clay sculpture." Again, she shifted toward me. "I asked my youngest son, Scott, to pose for me, so I could do a life- size bust in clay."

As she spoke, our van crept slowly toward the right lane. "When I finished the bust," Ellen said, "I wrapped it in clear plastic and put it in my freezer for storage until I could have it fired."

Now we were straddling lanes. I turned my head to see a red convertible one car length behind us in the right lane. Maybe they'd see us and pull back, I thought.

"Well, I forgot the thing was in there until my daughter came home from college," Ellen said. "She was helping me with dinner one night and I asked her to get some chicken out of the freezer." Ellen was facing me, laughing as she spoke. "I heard my daughter screaming and ran to see her holding her chest in front of the freezer door. Ha ha ha...." Ellen banged on the steering wheel as we swerved into the right lane. Instantly a searing horn blared from the convertible. Ellen whipped us back into our lane.

"Oops." Then right back to me she turned. " 'Well, Mom,' my daughter shouted, 'you always said one day Scott would push you too far!'" With that, Ellen practically laid her head on the steering wheel, as we swerved right back into the lane on top of the red convertible. Horns blasted again! Ellen waved in reply, "Sorry, sorry…" Ha, ha, ha! A few seconds later, Ellen jerked the wheel hard to the left. Our smoking, rattling van bounced up the driveway and screeched to a halt in front of my hotel lobby.

For a moment, I sat frozen, holding my breath. Slowly, my ticking, quivering nervous system began to uncoil with the realization that we had really made it. We were motionless. I was alive! Ellen still faced me beaming. "Well, Don, I can't tell you..." As she spoke, the bright red convertible with two young women inside, came zooming up next to us on Ellen's side, horn blowing, fists clenched, voices blaring.

"Hey you old _____!" they shouted. "Are you out of your _____ mind!!!"

Ellen stopped speaking mid-sentence and gave me a wink. With that, she turned and slowly began rolling down her window.

For Don's current teaching schedule,
gallery of paintings, and information on other
books and videos available, visit Don's website:

www.donandrews.net